C000056075

An Introduction to AutoCAD LT

BM7/ R141

An Introduction to AutoCAD LT

A. Yarwood

Registered Developer

Longman
Scientific &
Technical

Longman Scientific & Technical
Longman Group Limited
Longman House, Burnt Mill, Harlow
Essex CM20 2JE, England
and Associated Companies throughout the world

Copublished in the United States with
John Wiley & Sons, Inc., 605 Third Avenue, New York, NY 10158

© Longman Group Limited 1995

All rights reserved; no part of this publication may be reproduced, stored
in any retrieval system, or transmitted in any form or by any means,
electronic, mechanical, photocopying, recording, or otherwise without
either the prior written permission of the Publishers or a licence
permitting restricted copying in the United Kingdom issued by the
Copyright Licensing Agency Ltd, 90 Tottenham Court Road, London W1P
9HE.

First published 1995

British Library Cataloguing in Publication Data
A catalogue entry for this title is available from the British Library

ISBN 0-582-24617-2

Library of Congress Cataloging-in-Publication Data
A catalog entry for this title is available from the Library of Congress

ISBN 0-470-23555-1 (USA only)

Set by 24 in 10/13pt Melior
Produced by Longman Singapore Publishers (Pte) Ltd
Printed in Singapore

Contents

List of plates

Colour plates are between pages 114 and 115.

Preface

AutoCAD LT is primarily a 2D Computer Aided Design (CAD) software package which operates in Windows. As with other Windows applications it operates within the Windows environment – for example: it incorporates features such as Object Linking Embedding (OLE), allowing AutoCAD drawings to be included in documents created in applications such as word processors and DTP applications; it allows AutoCAD drawings to be saved as bitmap (*.bmp and *.wmp) files; it allows AutoCAD drawings to be transferred via the Windows Clipboard to other applications.

The package has a limited 3D capability in that, while not being able to create 3D meshes or faces, the creation of 3D lines, polylines and 3D elevations is possible. 3D solid models created in AutoCAD 11 or 12 can be loaded into AutoCAD LT to be viewed from a variety of angles and to be partly edited.

Unlike AutoCAD proper, the package does not include languages such as AutoLisp or any of the files developed with the AutoCAD Development System (ADS).

Taking into consideration that the vast majority of drawings in mechanical, electrical and electronics engineering as well as in building and architecture are two-dimensional (2D), the introduction of AutoCAD LT represents a major step forward in Autodesk software products.

Suitable for industry and commerce as a supplementary package to AutoCAD for Windows. Of particular interest to the author is that, because of its comparatively low cost, the purchase of AutoCAD LT is now possible by schools and colleges within their limited budgets, allowing them to run courses aimed at AutoCAD proper.

Hardware requirements

PC fitted with an 80386, 80486 or Pentium CPU.
If 80386, then an 80387 co-processor must be fitted.
A minimum of 4 Mbytes memory (RAM).
Hard disk, with at least 8 Mbytes of free space to allow AutoCAD LT files to load.

VGA, or preferably higher display monitor and video card.
A mouse.
No hardware lock ('dongle') is necessary.
Windows 3.1 or higher.
MS-DOS 3.3 or 5.0; preferably version 5.0, or higher.

Aims of the book

To provide a text covering sufficient details of the use of AutoCAD LT which is suitable for students in FE or HE or beginners to Computer Aided Design (CAD) wishing to learn how to use AutoCAD LT.

Acknowledgements

The author wishes to acknowledge with grateful thanks the help given to him by members of the staff at Autodesk Ltd.

Trademarks

The following are registered trademarks of Autodesk Inc.:

Autodesk®, AutoCAD®, AutoSketch®, AutoCAD LT®, Advanced Modeling Extension® (AME).

The following are trademarks of Autodesk Inc.:

ACAD™, DXF™, AutoCAD Development Interface™ (ADI), AutoCAD Development System™ (ADS).

IBM® is a registered trademark of the International Business Machines Corporation.

MS-DOS® is a registered trademark, and Windows™ is a trademark of the Microsoft Corporation.

A. Yarwood is a Registered Applications Developer with Autodesk Ltd.

Registered Developer

CHAPTER 1

Introduction

AutoCAD LT – an introduction

AutoCAD LT is primarily a two-dimensional (2D) Computer Aided Design (CAD) software package which operates in Windows. It has most of the 2D features found in the full AutoCAD for Windows, but has a very limited three-dimensional (3D) capability. 3D solid model drawings can be loaded into AutoCAD LT and partly edited, but 3D solid models cannot be constructed in AutoCAD LT. The software is therefore a simplified version of the full AutoCAD for Windows.

There are many advantages in using a CAD software package for constructing technical drawings. Among these are:

1. Any technical drawing which can be produced 'by hand' can be created in a CAD package.
2. Drawing with the aid of CAD is much quicker than working by hand. A skilled operator can produce drawings as much as 10 times as fast as when working by hand.
3. There is less tedium when working with CAD. Features such as text which can be rather tedious when entered freehand can be added to a drawing with the minimum of effort.
4. Drawings can be inserted into other drawings, without having to redraw them.
5. Parts of drawings can be copied, moved, mirrored, arrayed etc. without the need to redraw. In fact a basic rule when drawing with CAD is:

Never draw the same detail twice

6. Adding dimensions to a drawing is very fast and, when using associative dimensioning, reduces the possibility of dimensioning error.
7. Drawings created in CAD can be saved as files on a disk system, considerably reducing the amount of space required for the storage of drawings.

8. Drawings can be printed or plotted to any scale from the same drawing, reducing the need to make a separate drawing for each scale.

There are some disadvantages when comparing hand drawing with CAD drawing, the most serious being the initial expense in the setting up of the necessary equipment, particularly in a large design office. There is also the disadvantage that CAD is sometimes unsuitable for the making of design sketches, many of which may need to be drawn freehand. A further disadvantage lies in the need to fully train an operator new to CAD draughting.

Equipment required for working with AutoCAD LT

Software

AutoCAD LT software.
MS-DOS Versions 3.3 or higher.
Windows 3.1 or higher.

Hardware

PC fitted with an 80386, 80486 or Pentium CPU.
If 80386 or 80486 of the SX series, then an 80387 co-processor must be fitted.
A minimum of 4 Mbytes memory (RAM).
Hard disk, with at least 8 Mbytes of free space to allow AutoCAD LT files to load.
VGA or, preferably, higher display monitor and video card.
A mouse.

Fig. 1.1 shows a typical setup for running AutoCAD LT. The computer shown has a 'tower' type case, but the more common desk top type case is just as suitable. The VDU shown has a 14 inch screen, but if costs allow, it is preferable to work with any CAD package on a larger screen – 17 inch or larger.

The GUI of AutoCAD LT and Windows

The Windows software is based on a Graphical User Interface (GUI) which involves:

1. The 'windows' in which everything worked in Windows will appear – Fig. 1.2.
2. Icons representing applications, commands, tools and other features of the software – Fig. 1.2.
3. Operations under the control of a mouse – a pointing and selection device with two switches, known as 'buttons' with which all operations are performed by:

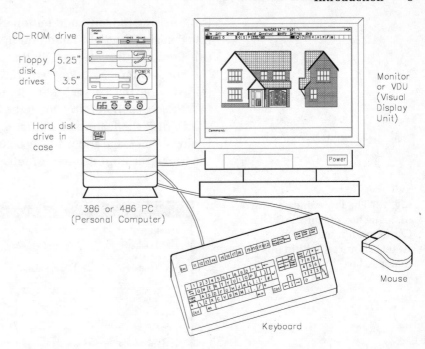

Fig. 1.1 A typical hardware
setup for AutoCAD LT

(a) Moving the mouse over the surface of the desk on which the
     computer stands. A cursor in the form of an arrow, a cross or
     cursor lines moves in response to movement of the mouse –
     Fig. 1.2;

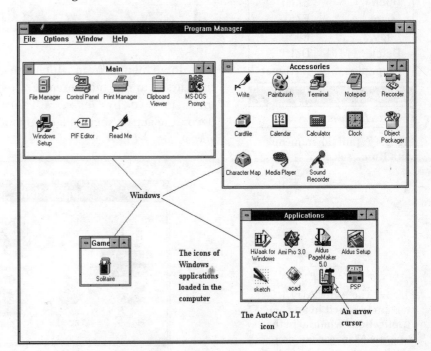

Fig. 1.2 The **Program Manager**
'window' of Windows 3.1
showing windows, icons and
an arrow cursor

(b) Pressing the left-hand button of the mouse – a *left-click*;

(c) Pressing the right-hand button of the mouse – a *right-click*;

(d) Pressing the left-hand button of the mouse twice in quick succession – a *double-left-click*;

(e) Moving the cursor under mouse control over a feature on screen, then holding down the button and moving the mouse to *drag* the feature to a different position on screen.

4. Dialogue, message and warning boxes which guide the operator in the use of the application currently on screen – Fig. 1.3.

Fig. 1.3 The **Preferences** dialogue box of AutoCAD LT. Configuration settings for AutoCAD are set within this dialogue box

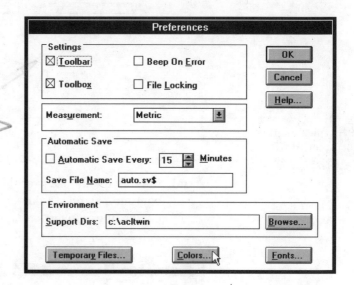

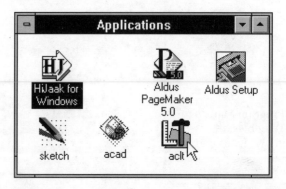

Fig. 1.4 A pull-down menu with **Run...** selected

5. Pull-down menus, from which a selection can be made by moving the cursor under mouse control over a name in the pull-down menu, followed by a *left-click*. This will result in the named feature becoming active such as a command, bringing a dialogue box on screen etc. – Fig. 1.4.

Fig. 1.5 The AutoCAD LT start-up icon **aclt** in an Applications window in the **Program Manager** window

Fig. 1.6 The AutoCAD LT box which appears in its own window when AutoCAD LT is started up

Fig. 1.7 The AutoCAD LT graphics window

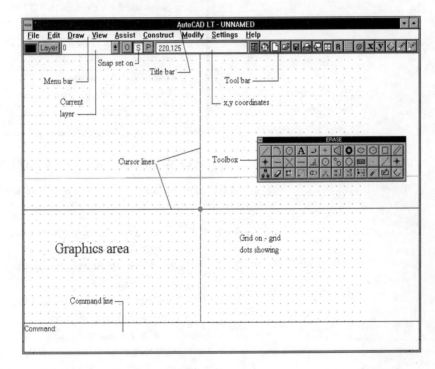

Fig. 1.8 The **File** pull-down menu

Starting up AutoCAD LT

Depending upon the way in which the computer being operated has been configured, AutoCAD is usually started up by a *double-left-click* on the **aclt** icon found in the **Program Manager** window of Windows – Fig. 1.5. The box shown in Fig. 1.6 briefly appears in its own window, followed a few seconds later by the AutoCAD LT graphics window – Fig. 1.7. The various features of the graphics window are named in this illustration. If AutoCAD LT has already been configured to show a suitable screen for the operator's drawing, he/she can immediately commence constructing the required drawing. Further steps may be required if the screen has not already been configured in a manner suitable for the required drawing parameters.

Fig. 1.9 The **Preferences**
dialogue box

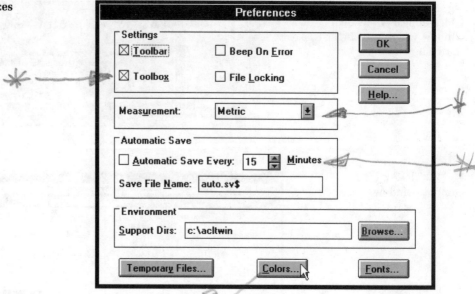

Configuring the AutoCAD LT graphic window

If the graphics window is not set up as desired, configurations can
be changed by:

1. *Left-click* on **File** in the Menu bar. The **File** pull-down menu
   appears – Fig. 1.8.
2. *Left-click* on **Preferences...** in the menu. The **Preferences** dialogue
   box appears – Fig. 1.9.
3. In the dialogue box note the graphics window can be set:
   (a) to show a **Toolbar** or not;
   (b) to show a **Toolbox** or not;
   (c) to lock drawing files when they have been saved;
   (d) to sound a beep when an error occurs;
   (e) to set the unit of measurement – in the example this is **Metric**;
   (f) to save drawings automatically at any set interval of time;
   (g) to obtain different colours for the parts of the graphics window;
   (h) to set the font showing in the Command line and in the
       Toolbar.

The reader is advised to experiment with these settings and to set
them as desired for his/her own purposes.

Notes

1. The *check* boxes to the left of **Toolbar**, **Toolbox** and **Automatic
   Save Every**. A *left-click* with the cursor arrow inside these boxes
   will either change a blank box to one with a cross, or vice versa. If

a box contains a cross it is said to be *checked* and the item against which it is placed is **ON**. If the check box is empty, the item is **OFF** – that is it is not functioning.

2. If three full stops appear after a name in a dialogue box or in a pull-down menu, it means that when that name is selected a dialogue box will appear to allow further settings to be made. Thus if **Colors...** in the **Preferences** dialogue box is selected, a further dialogue box appears named **AutoCAD LT Window Colors**, in which the colours of the various parts of the graphics window can be set.

3. If necessary some of the colours of the AutoCAD LT graphics window may need to be set in the Windows **Program Manager** – a *double-left-click* on the **Control Panel** icon, followed by another on the **Colors** icon, brings up the **Color** dialogue box associated with Windows. Colours set in this dialogue box affect all applications running under Windows – of which AutoCAD LT is one.

4. By all means change the font if desired.

5. It is not really advisable to engage **File Locking**, unless working in a network system or on a computer which others will be using. The idea of File locking is to prevent others from using your drawing files.

The toolbox

Fig. 1.10 is an enlarged illustration of the toolbox. This contains the tools (or commands) which are used when constructing a drawing. Thus the Toolbox contains tools such as for drawing a **LINE**, for drawing a **CIRCLE** etc. Try placing the cursor arrow under mouse control over an icon in the toolbox. The name of the tool represented by the icon appears in the title bar of the toolbox window. This allows for easy selection of the tools as and when they are required, although you will find that you learn what the icons represent after a very short period of using the software.

Customising the Toolbox

The toolbox can be customised to meet the requirements of the operator. This is carried out in the **Toolbox Customization** dialogue box, called by moving the cursor over any icon in the toolbox,

Fig 1.10 The **Toolbox**

Fig. 1.11 The **Toolbox Customization** dialogue box

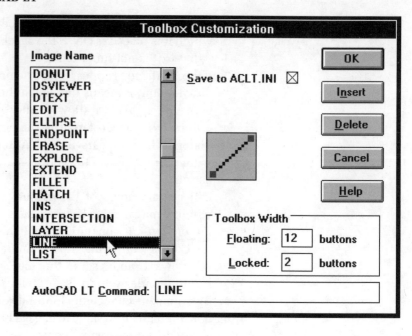

Fig. 1.12 A Toolbox of 5 buttons' width

followed by a *right-click*. The dialogue box then appears – Fig. 1.11. The icon over which a *right-click* was made appears in the centre of the dialogue box. *Left-click* on the name of a tool in the file list and the icon in the centre of the dialogue box changes. The new icon can then be inserted into the toolbox by a *left-click* on the **Insert** button. The selected icon appears in the toolbox. An icon shown in both the toolbox and the dialogue box can be deleted from the toolbox by a *left-click* on the **Delete** button.

The rectangular shape of the toolbox can be amended by *entering* a new number in the box to the right of **Floating:** in the **Toolbox Width** box. In addition as many of the tools can be locked within the toolbox as required by *entering* a number in the **Locked:** box. Fig. 1.12 shows a toolbox of 5 buttons' (icons) width.

Fig. 1.13 The **Control Panel** icon in the **Main** window of the Windows **Program Manager**

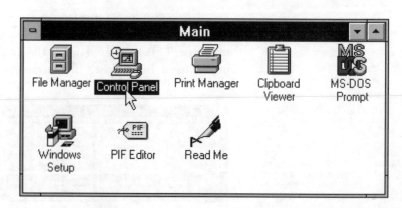

Fig. 1.14 The **Colors** icon in the **Control Panel**

Configuring AutoCAD LT from Windows Control Panel

It may be necessary to change some of the colours of the parts of the AutoCAD LT graphics window within the Windows **Program Manager** as follows:

1. *Left-click* on the **Control Panel** icon in the **main** window of the **Program manager** – Fig. 1.13, followed by a *left-click* on the **Colors** icon in the **Control Panel** dialogue box – Fig. 1.14.
2. *Left-click* on the **Colors** icon in the dialogue box. The **Color** dialogue box appears – Fig. 1.15.
3. *Left-click* on **Color Palette>>** in the dialogue box. A colour palette appears.

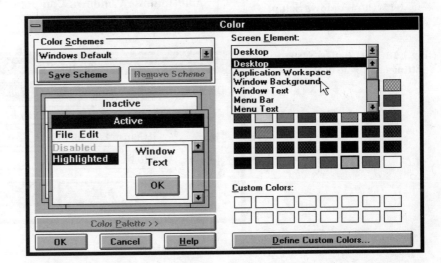

Fig 1.15 The **Color** dialogue box

4. *Left-click on* the word(s) appearing in the **Screen Element** box and a *pop-up* list appears showing all the parts of any of the windows – of which the AutoCAD LT graphics window is one.
5. *Left-click* on the required part for which you require a colour change, followed by another *left-click* on the desired colour in the palette. Note the changes in that part of the dialogue box showing the various parts of a miniature Windows window.

Other changes affecting the configuration of AutoCAD LT may require setting from the **Control Panel** of Windows. These include the settings for the Visual Display Unit (VDU). Although AutoCAD will work with a Visual Graphics Adaptor (VGA) better results are obtained with a higher type of VDU giving a higher resolution – more pixels on the screen. In the examples shown throughout this book a Super Video Graphics Adaptor (SVGA) driver was used. The configuration for the driver (a Windows driver) was set through the Windows

Fig. 1.16 The **Setup** icon from the **Main** window in the **Program Manager**

Setup program. A *double-left-click* on the **Setup** icon (Fig. 1.16) in the **Main** window of the **Program Manager** brings up the **Windows Setup** dialogue box – Fig. 1.17. A *left-click* on **Change Systems Settings...** and the **Change System Settings** dialogue box appears – Fig. 1.18. Within this box, the settings for the **Display**, the **Mouse** and the **Keyboard** can be made and if the computer is on a network the network configuration can be set.

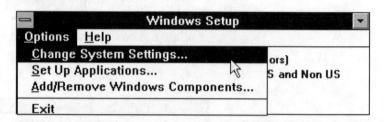

Fig. 1.17 The **Windows Setup** dialogue box

Fig 1.18 The **Change System Settings** dialogue box

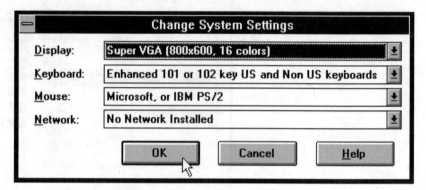

Questions

1. What are the major differences between the AutoCAD LT and AutoCAD for Windows?
2. Why is it that the statement *Never draw the same thing twice* applies so well to drawing with a CAD package?
3. Can you state any disadvantages in using CAD as against drawing by hand?
4. What are the minimum hardware requirements for running AutoCAD LT?
5. What does the abbreviation GUI stand for?
6. What is meant by the term GUI?
7. What is meant by the following terms:
   left-click?
   right-click?
   double-left-click?
   cursor?
   dragging?

8. What is a dialogue box?
9. What is the purpose of dialogue boxes?
10. Which settings for AutoCAD LT may have to be made in Windows?
11. What happens with a *left-click* on a name in a pull-down menu or in a dialogue box which ends with three fullstops (...)?
12. What is a tool in AutoCAD LT?
13. How are tool icons changed in the toolbox?

CHAPTER 2

Methods of operation

Fig. 2.1 The **Settings** Short
Menu

Settings
Short Menu
Aerial View
Toolbox Style

Entity Modes...
Drawing Aids...
Layer Control...

Linetype Style ▶
Text Style...
Dimension Style...
√ Associative Dimensions
Polyline Style ▶
Point Style...

Units Style...
Grips Style...
Selection Style...

Drawing ▶

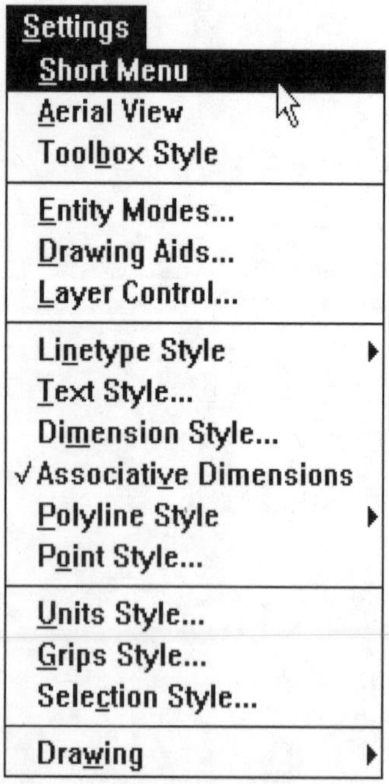

Fig. 2.2. The **Settings** Full
Menu

Introduction

As stated in Chapter 1 AutoCAD LT operates within a Graphical
User Interface(GUI) system involving icons, pull-down menus and
dialogue boxes. The system can also be operated if wished by
entering instructions from the keyboard. The icons are found either
in the **Toolbar** or in the **Toolbox** (see Fig. 1.10). Icons can be added
to or deleted from the toolbar or toolbox. The pull-down menus can
be in either a **Short Menu** or a **Full Menu** form depending on how the
operator wishes to work. The dialogue boxes are in *windows and* are
of three types:

1. Dialogue boxes in which settings can be made.
2. Warning boxes informing the operator of possible errors which
   may occur.
3. Message boxes with messages pertinent to the operation taking
   place.

If operating the system by entering instructions at the keyboard,
these can be entered either in full or as abbreviations.

The pull-down menus

A *left-click* on **Settings** in the Menu bar brings the **Settings** pull-
down menu onto the screen. If in the **Short Menu** – Fig. 2.1 – either
a *left-click* on **Full Menu** or *entering* an f at the keyboard changes the
menu into a full one. Similarly if in the **Full Menu** – Fig. 2.2 – a *left-
click on* **Short Menu** changes the menu into a short one. Note that
this short and full form of menu applies to all pull-down menus.
Thus the form of all pull-down menus – short or full – is set in the
Settings menu. Features common to all pull-down menus can be
seen in Fig. 2.2:

1. A feature is *called* from a pull-down menu by either:
   Moving the screen cursor under control of the mouse over the name
   followed by a *left-click*,

or

If a letter in the name is underlined, *entering* that letter at the keyboard – but **only** while the pull-down menu is showing on screen.

2. A *left-click* on a name in a pull-down menu causes the name to highlight – the letters of the name change colour (e.g. black to white) and the area around the name changes colour (e.g. to black).

3. If a name is followed by three full stops (**...**) a *left-click* over that name brings up a dialogue box on screen. Thus a *left-click* on **Drawing Aids...**, the name highlights and the **Drawing Aids** dialogue box appears on screen – Fig. 2.3.

Fig. 2.3 The **Drawing Aids** dialogue box

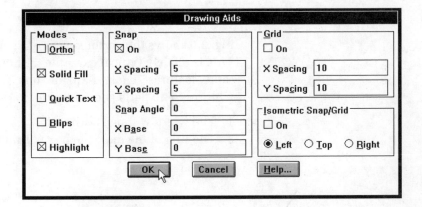

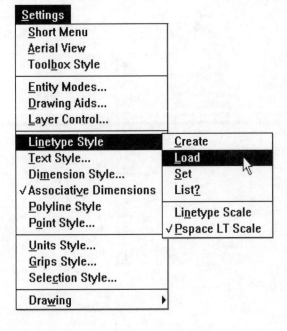

Fig. 2.4 The **Linetype Style** sub-menu

4. A tick against a name means that the feature is active. Thus from the **Settings** menu – Fig. 2.2 – it can be seen that **Associative Dimensions** are in operation when including dimensions in a drawing. A *left-click* on **Associative Dimensions** while the tick is showing and the feature becomes inactive. A *left-click* on the name when no tick is showing renders the feature active again. Only a minority of menu features use this facility.

5. A small arrow pointing outwards from a menu name shows that a sub-menu associated with the feature will appear with a *left-click* over the name. An example is given in Fig. 2.4 in which the **Linetype Style** sub-menu is brought on screen by a *left-click over* the name.

The parts of a dialogue box

Fig. 2.5 shows the various parts of the **Open Drawing** dialogue box. This is a fairly typical example, although not all boxes contain the same features. Each dialogue box is contained within its own window. The parts shown in Fig. 2.5 are:

1. The window frame outline.
2. The title of the dialogue box within the title bar of the box.

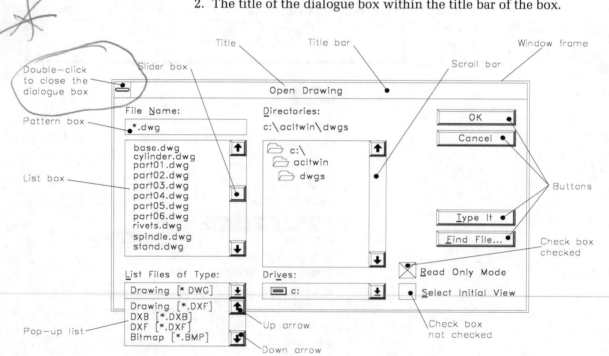

Fig. 2.5 The parts of a dialogue box

3. The button at the top left of some dialogue boxes by which the box can be closed.

4. The List box in which are lists of the files from which one can choose to open. Either a *double-left-click* on a selected filename, or a *left-click* on the name, which highlights, followed by a *left-click* on the **OK** button.

5. A pattern box in which the name of the type of file is displayed. The * in front of the filename extension is known as a *wildcard* – *.dwg means all files that have the 'dwg' extension.

6. The Slider box within a Scroll bar. If the List box contains more names than can be accommodated within the area in the dialogue box, further names can be seen by either moving the Slider box in the scroll bar or by *left-clicks* on the Up and/or Down arrows.

7. A Pop-up list. A left-click on the name in the box of the Pop-up brings down a List box containing options from which one can make a choice. The **Drives** box will provide another Pop-up list showing the disk drives available on the computer in use.

8. Buttons. Of those shown in Fig. 2.5 a *left-click* on **OK** will cause the dialogue box to close and the selected drawing to appear. *Left-click* on **Cancel** to close the box without any other action taking place. *Left-click* on **Type It** and the filename will need to be *entered* from the keyboard. *Left-click* on **Find File...** and the **Find File** dialogue box appears.

9. Check boxes. A cross appearing in a box shows it is checked and the feature will be in operation. A *left-click* on a checked box unchecks it, makes the feature inoperative and the cross disappears.

A more common form of dialogue box is shown in Fig. 2.6 in which some of the parts of that shown in Fig. 2.5 are not present. In this dialogue box – **Drawing Aids** – settings can be made by entering numbers or checking/unchecking in the various boxes against the

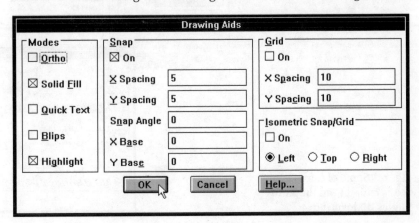

Fig. 2.6 The **Drawing Aids** dialogue box

names of the features which can be configured in this box. **Snap** and **Grid** spacings can be entered as numbers. **Ortho** (all lines etc. drawn only horizontally or vertically), **Solid Fill** (for entities such as Plines), **Blips** (small crosses appearing at each point selected in the graphics area by the mouse) and **Highlight** can be either on or off (boxes with cross or empty). The settings for drawing along isometric axes can also be set in either a check box or a check circle. In a check circle a *left-click* makes a solid dot appear (feature set **ON**) or if the dot is present a *left-click* turns the feature **OFF**.

Dragging dialogue boxes

Dialogue boxes can be placed anywhere on screen by *dragging* with the aid of the mouse. Move the screen cursor onto the title bar of the dialogue box and, holding down the left mouse button, move the mouse. The dialogue box then moves with the mouse movement. This movement under mouse control is what is known as *dragging*. Fig. 2.7 shows three boxes, the first **Entity Creation Modes** selected with a *left-click* on **Entity Modes...** in the **Settings** pull-down menu. The second came on screen with a *left-click* on the **Text Style...** button. The third appears with a *left-click* on **Show All...** in the **Text Style** dialogue box. In between each dialogue box was moved by being *dragged* to a new position with the mouse.

Dialogue boxes called by entering dd****

Some of the dialogue boxes can be called by entering the name of the dialogue box preceded by the two letters **dd**:

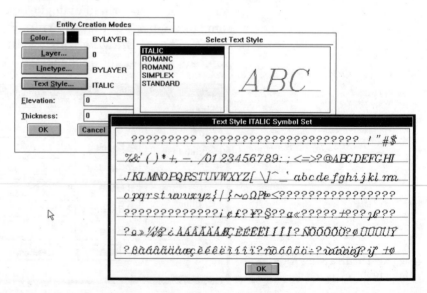

Fig. 2.7 Some of the dialogue boxes called from the **Entity Modes** dialogue box

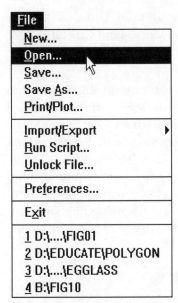

Fig. 2.8 The **File** pull-down menu

enter ddattext	**Attribute Extraction** dialogue box appears.
enter ddedit	**Edit Text** dialogue box appears.
enter ddemodes	**Entity Creation Modes** dialogue box appears.
enter ddgrips	**Grips** dialogue box appears.
enter ddinsert	**Insert** dialogue box appears.
enter ddlmodes	**Layer Control** dialogue box appears.
enter ddosnap	**Running Object Snap** dialogue box appears.
enter ddrename	**Rename** dialogue box appears.
enter ddrmodes	**Drawing Aids** dialogue box appears.
enter ddselect	**Entity Selection Settings** dialogue box appears.

The boxes can also be brought on screen by selection from pull-down menus.

Pull-down menus

Some references were made to pull-down menus in Chapter 1- Figures 1.4 and 1.8. The other pull-downs called by *left-clicks* on the menu names in the menu bar are shown in Figures 2.8 to 2.15. Some of the features whose names appear in the menus have sub-menus – those with an outward pointing arrow to the right of the name. Some of these are shown in the illustrations of the pull-downs.

The File pull-down menu

Fig. 2.8. The menu from which file commands are chosen. In addition the **Preferences** dialogue box can be called for configuring the graphics window (see Chapter 1). Two other commands from this menu are **Exit**, the selection of which takes the operator out of AutoCAD and back to the **Program Manager** window and **Print/ Plot...** which will bring up the dialogue box from which settings are made for either printing or plotting drawings. Note that the numbered names at the bottom of this menu are the previously four loaded AutoCAD files. A *left-click* on any one of these filenames will bring the drawing associated with the filename back on screen.

The Edit pull-down menu

Fig. 2.9. The **Undo** and **Redo** commands from this menu either undo the last command to be called or bring back a feature which has been undone. Repeated use of **Undo** will eventually undo everything that has been constructed in the graphics window. However, **Redo** only brings back the action of the very last **Undo**. The **Copy** commands are for taking drawings or parts of drawings to *Paste* into other drawings or windows from other Windows applications, such as a word

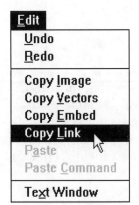

Fig. 2.9 The **Edit** pull-down menu

processor. A *left-click* on **Text Window** and the AutoCAD LT text window replaces the graphics window. More about this later.

The View pull-down menu

Fig. 2.10. This menu includes the very important **Zoom** and **Pan** commands, by which the smallest area of the screen can be examined or worked in with accuracy. Apart from **Redraw**, which enables a fast redrawing of the screen when necessary and **Regen**, which allows a complete, thorough redrawing, the other commands in this menu are mostly concerned with the partial three-dimensional possibilities with AutoCAD LT. It will have been noted that several of the features in this menu will show sub-menus when selected. Note also the greyed-out name – showing that it is not available.

Fig. 2.10 The **View** pull-down menu

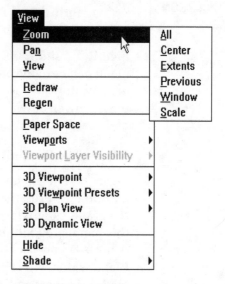

The Draw pull-down menu

Fig. 2.11. Depending upon how you intend creating drawings in AutoCAD LT, this menu is one which may be in use more than any other because it contains most of the command names of the tools which will be used for actually constructing drawing. Note that a number of the commands have sub-menus, one of which, that for **Circle**, is included in Fig. 2.11.

The Assist pull-down menu

Fig. 2.12. A number of features in this menu are associated with the limited 3D capability of AutoCAD LT. Of the others **Object Snap** is of great value for assisting in obtaining accurate constructions. The

Fig. 2.11 The **Draw** pull-down menu

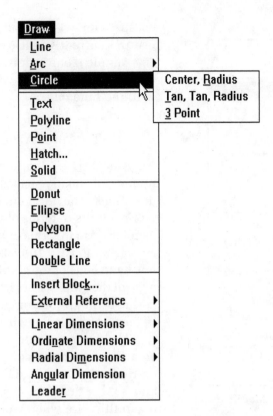

Fig. 2.12 The **Assist** pull-down menu

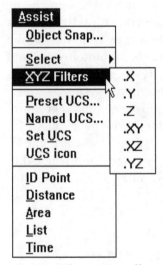

four features at the bottom of the menu are concerned with determining positions, sizes, areas, timing in drawings on screen.

The Construct pull-down menu

Fig. 2.13. The features in this menu extend constructions already carried out with the aid of the **Draw** commands. The use of blocks will be described in Chapter 7. An attribute is text which can be added to parts of a drawing. Text defined as an attribute can be, but need not be, included with the part to which it refers.

The Modify pull-down menu

Fig. 2.14. As the name of the menu suggests, the features in this menu are for modifying constructions already in the graphics area of the screen. The names of the commands are self-explanatory and their functions will be explained in detail in a later chapter.

The Help pull-down menu

Fig. 2.15. Extensive help text is available for all features of AutoCAD LT. The **Help** pull-down menu need, in fact to be rarely called

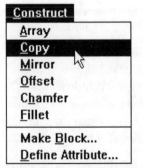

Fig. 2.13 The **Construct** pull-down menu

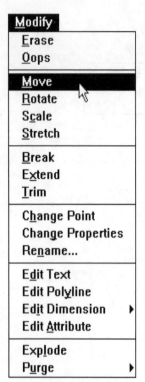

Fig. 2.14 The **Modify** pull-down menu

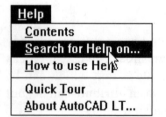

Fig. 2.15 The **Help** pull-down menu

because context-sensitive help can be obtained for the command or features currently in use by pressing the **F1** key of the keyboard. As an example if one is drawing with the **Line** command tool, pressing the **F1** key brings up a window with text explaining how to work with the **Line** tool.

The AutoCAD LT coordinate system

An AutoCAD LT graphics area can be said to be divided into a number of equally spaced units in both the horizontal and vertical directions. The horizontal units can be stated in terms of x and the vertical units in terms of y. This enables any point on the screen to be referred to in terms of x units and y units, any one position being given as, e.g. $x,y = 100,50$, – a point 100 units horizontally from the left-hand edge of the graphics area and 50 units up from the bottom edge of the graphics area. The point $x,y = 0,0$ is the bottom left-hand corner of the graphics area. This system of dividing an area into units in terms of x,y is known as a Cartesian coordinate system.

The x,y coordinate of the top right-hand corner of the graphics area is set with the command **Limits**. The following sequence of entries at the Command line sets the x,y coordinates of the graphics area so that drawings can be constructed as if each unit is equal to one millimetre when working to a scale of full size on an A3 size drawing sheet:

Command: *enter* limits *right-click*
ON/OFF/<Lower left hand corner><0,0>: *right-click*
Upper right corner<12,9>: *enter* 420,297 *right-click*
Command: *enter* z (for Zoom) *right-click*
All/Center/Extents/Previous/Window/Scale(X/XP): *enter* a
(for All) *right-click*
Command:

Notes

1. The type in **bold** letters is what appears at the command line.
2. *enter* means type at the keyboard the letters or word which follow.
3. The line showing **All/Center/Extents/Previous/Window/Scale(X/XP):** shows the *prompts* which are available when using **Zoom**. Entering an initial capital letter of one of the prompts at the keyboard determines which prompt is selected. Thus:

enter a (for All) and all the area within the limits fills the graphics area.

(for Center) allows a central point for the coordinate system

...ver has been drawn on the screen,
...system or outside it appears in

...e had been a previous zoom, the

...ea of the graphics window can be
...of the operator's choice.

...shows as **<Scale(X/XP)>**. Without
...er a scale figure – e.g. 0.5 and the
...size. *Enter* 2 and any features in the
...scale.

...in brackets < > show what is known as
...s the upper right-hand corner before
...12,9.

...this is the size in millimetres of an A3

...he limits will not be set until the graphics
...the units covering the whole graphics area.

An example ...**oordinate points**

Make sure the AutoCAD LT graphics window is set to limits as described earlier. Then:

1. *Left-click* on **Settings** in the menu bar, followed by a *left-click* on **Points Style...** in the pull-down menu. The **Points Style dialogue** box appears.
2. In the **points Style** box, *left-click* on the point shape as shown in Fig. 2.16, followed by a *left-click* on the **OK** button. The point style is now set.
3. At the command line enter the following:

    > **Command:** *enter* point *right-click*
    > **Point:** *enter* 80,80 *right-click*
    > **Command:** *right-click* (calls back the Point command)
    > **POINT Point:** *enter* 160,95 *right-click*
    > **Command:** *right-click*
    > **POINT Point:** *enter* 95,235 *right-click*
    > **Command:** *right-click*
    > **POINT Point:** *enter* 220,165 *right-click*
    > **Command:** *right-click*
    > **POINT Point:** *enter* 300,235 *right-click*

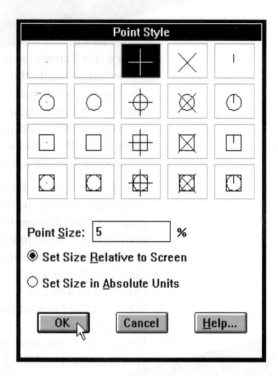

Fig. 2.16 Choosing a Point style

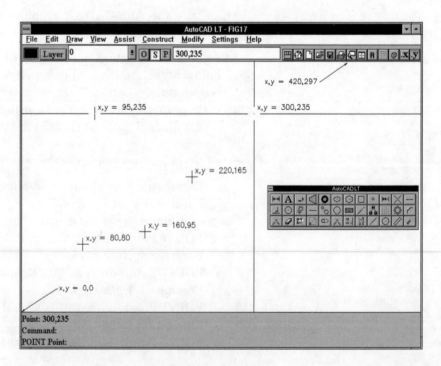

Fig. 2.17 An AutoCAD LT graphics window showing points at stated coordinate positions

Command: *right-click*
POINT Point: *enter* 420,297 *right-click*
Command:

The result will be as shown in Fig. 2.17, with the chosen point at each of the stated coordinate points.

Note the changes in the figures for the coordinates in the Coordinates window in the toolbar as the coordinate numbers are entered at the command line – Fig. 2.18 gives an example.

Fig. 2.18 The coordinates window in the toolbar when coordinates for the point at 330,225 are entered

The four methods of calling commands for drawing

There are four ways in which drawing commands or *Tools* can be called into use in AutoCAD LT. These are:

1. By selecting a tool icon from the toolbox. Fig. 2.19 shows the **Line** tool being selected – cursor arrow placed over the line icon, the name of the tool appears in the title bar of the toolbox. *Left-click* and the command line changes to:

    Command: LINE From point:

Fig. 2.19 The **LINE** icon selected from the toolbox

2. *Left-click* on **Draw** in the menu bar. *Left-click* on **Line** in the menu. The command line changes to

    Command:_Line From point:

3. *enter* line at the keyboard. The command line changes to:

    Command: *enter* line *right-click*
    From point:

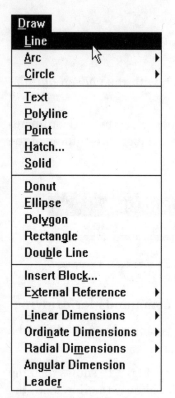

Fig. 2.20 **Line** selected from the **Draw** pull-down menu

4. *Enter* l (abbreviation for Line) at the keyboard. The command line changes to:

> **Command:** *enter* l *right-click*
> **LINE From point:**

Notes

1. No matter which of the four methods of working is used, the prompts at the command line will be similar. It is up to the operator which of the methods he/she employs.
2. In AutoCAD LT there are abbreviations for all commands. See the Appendix on p. 208.
3. The two words 'command' and 'tool' have much the same meaning.
4. If you cannot think of its abbreviation, remember that the full name can be entered at any time to operate a command.

Drawing lines, circles and arcs

No matter which method of drawing is chosen – selecting tool icons, selecting from pull-down menus, entering the full command name or entering an abbreviation – the prompts associated with each command always appear at the command line. This means that the following descriptions of the commands and command prompts will be the same, or very similar, no matter which method of working is adopted.

In practice, most operators will use a mixture of methods – for example, the most frequently used **Draw** tools chosen from the toolbox or toolbar icons, with less frequently used commands entered as abbreviations, some being entered in full while a few will be selected from pull-down menus.

Lines

Left-click on the **LINE** icon in the toolbox. The command line shows:

> **Command: LINE From point:** Move the line cursors under mouse control to any position on screen and *left-click*. The command line changes to
> **To point:** Move the cursors again to another position and *left-click*. The command line again changes to
> **To point:**

Repeat several times without bothering about what is being drawn. When satisfied that you understand how to draw lines at random, *right-click*. The command line reverts to:

Command:

Circles

Enter c from the keyboard. The command line changes to:

> **Command: CIRCLE 3P/TTR/<Center point>:** *left-click* anywhere on screen. The command line changes to
>
> **Radius:** *left-click* at another point. A circle appears
>
> **Command:** *right-click* – brings back
>
> **CIRCLE 3P/TTR/<Center point>** *enter* 3p *right-click*. The command line changes
>
> **First point:** *left-click* at any point on screen
>
> **Second point:** *left-click* at another point on screen
>
> **Third point:** *left-click* at a third point on screen. A circle appears
>
> **Command:** *right-click* brings back
>
> **CIRCLE 3P/TTR/<Center point>** *enter* ttr *right-click*. The command line changes to
>
> **Enter Tangent spec:** *left-click* on your first circle. The command line changes to
>
> **Enter second Tangent spec:** *left-click* on your second circle. The command line changes to:
>
> **Radius:** either enter a suitable figure or *left-click* on two points on the screen some distance apart. A circle, tangential to your other two circles appears. The command line reverts to
>
> **Command:**

Arcs

Left-click on **Draw** in the menu bar, followed by a *left-click* on **Arc** in the menu. The **Arc** sub-menu appears – Fig. 2.21. Depending upon which of the selections is made in the sub-menu, the command line changes to:

> **Command:_arc Center/<Start point>:** with added prompts for some of the selections.

Taking as an example the **3 point** selection, the following series of prompts appear at the command line:

> **Command:_arc Center/<Start point>:** *left-click* at any point on screen. The command line changes to
>
> **Center/End/<Second point>:** *left-click* an another point. The command line changes to
>
> **End point:** *left-click* at the end point of the arc. The arc appears on screen and the command line reverts to
>
> **Command:**

Fig. 2.22 shows the results of the use of these three commands.

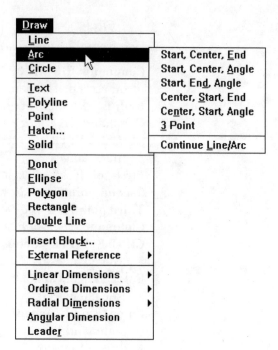

Fig. 2.21 The **Arc** sub-menu from the **Draw** pull-down menu

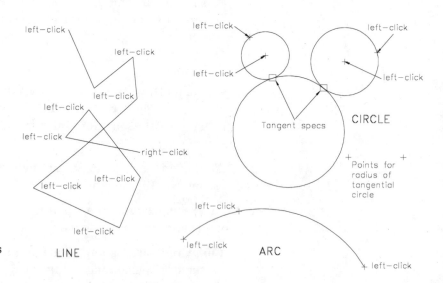

Fig. 2.22 Random lines, circles and arc

Absolute and relative coordinates

In order to construct drawings which are accurate as to sizes, use either the absolute coordinate or the relative coordinate methods. These involve keying coordinate numbers at the command line from the keyboard.

The absolute coordinate method

This entails entering the coordinate numbers for each point on a drawing. Fig. 2.23 is an example of a simple outline constructed with the aid of the **LINE** tool using the absolute coordinate method. This example was constructed as follows:

Fig. 2.23 An outline drawing with **LINE** using absolute coordinates

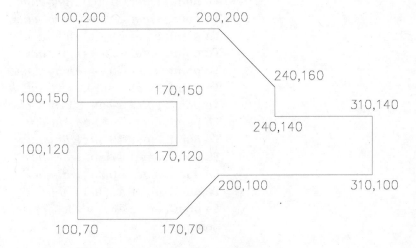

Left-click on the **LINE** icon in the toolbox. Then type in the following coordinate numbers at the command line:

Command: LINE From point: *enter* 100,200 *right-click*
To point: *enter* 200,200 *right-click*
To point: *enter* 240,160 *right-click*
To point: *enter* 240,140 *right-click*
To point: *enter* 310,140 *right-click*
To point: *enter* 310,100 *right-click*
To point: *enter* 200,100 *right-click*
To point: *enter* 170,70 *right-click*
To point: *enter* 100,70 *right-click*
To point: *enter* 100,120 *right-click*
To point: *enter* 170,120 *right-click*
To point: *enter* 170,150 *right-click*
To point: *enter* 100,150 *right-click*
To point: *enter* c (for Close) *right-click*
Command:

The relative coordinate method

Using this method involves entering coordinate numbers which are relative to the previously entered coordinate. Using the same drawing example as was used to illustrate the absolute coordinate method, the same outline would be constructed as follows:

Left-click on the **LINE** icon in the toolbox and then enter the following using @ before the coordinate numbers.

Command: LINE From point: *enter* 100,200 *right-click*
To point: *enter* @100,0 *right-click*
To point: *enter* @40,–40 *right-click*
To point: *enter* @0,–20 *right-click*
To point: *enter* @70,0 *right-click*
To point: *enter* @0,–40 *right-click*
To point: *enter* @–110,0 *right-click*
To point: *enter* @–30,–30 *right-click*
To point: *enter* @–70,0 *right-click*
To point: *enter* @0,50 *right-click*
To point: *enter* @70,0 *right-click*
To point: *enter* @0,30 *right-click*
To point: *enter* @–70,0 *right-click*
To point: *enter* @c (for Close) *right-click*
Command:

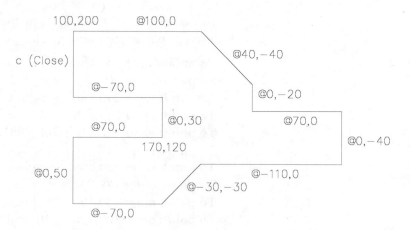

Fig. 2.24 An outline drawn with **LINE** to relative coordinates

Notes
1. @ must precede relative coordinate numbers.
2. +ve *x* coordinate numbers are to the right.
3. –ve *x* coordinate numbers are to the left.
4. +ve *y* coordinate numbers are upwards.
5. –ve *y* coordinate numbers are downwards.
6. –ve *x* and –ve *y* coordinate numbers are to the left and below.
7. +ve *x* and +ve *y* numbers are above and to the right.

8. The advantage of using relative coordinates is that the unit length of each part of a construction can be entered in the coordinate number.
9. Note the use of c (for Close) to close an outline.

Grid and Snap

Grid and **Snap** can be set either by entering figures in the appropriate boxes in the **Drawing Aids** dialogue box – see Fig. 2.3 on page 13 – or from the command line. Thus to set **Grid** from the command line:

> **Command:** *enter* grid *right-click*
> **Grid spacing(X) or ON/OFF/Snap/Aspect<1>:** *enter* 10   *right-click*
> **Command:**

To set **Snap** from the command line:

> **Command:** *enter* snap *right-click*
> **Snap spacing or ON/OFF/Aspect/Rotate/Style<1>:** *enter* 5 *right-click*
> **Command:**

The variety of prompts in the grid and snap series will be explained in later chapters – they are of importance mainly when dealing with pictorial drawing.

When **Grid** is on – either set **On** by checking the check box in the **Drawing Aids** dialogue box, or by entering on in answer to the prompts at the command line, or by pressing the function key of the keyboard **F7**. When set on, a series of grid dots appears on screen spaced at the interval as set – in the example above the grid dots will appear at 10 unit intervals both vertically and horizontally. The grid dots form a useful pattern for guidance of an operator for a variety of purposes. The easiest way to set grid dots on or off is by pressing the **F7** key – it 'toggles' between setting grid on and off.

When snap is **ON** – either set **On** in the check box of the **Drawing Aids** dialogue box, by entering on at the command line, or by pressing key **F9** (the toggle for snap on or off) – as the cursor is moved under mouse control, it will move in jerks, snapping from one snap point to another. Snap is a useful aid to accuracy particularly when constructing drawings, the entities of which are in snap distance lengths. Snap is a useful tool in a variety of constructions, which individual operators can use to advantage in different ways.

Note

Use **F7** and **F9** to toggle grid and snap on/off once they have been set.

Object snaps or Osnaps

Object snaps can be set in the **Running Object Snap** dialogue box –
Fig. 2.25. A *left-click on* **Assist** in the menu bar, followed by another
left-click on **Object Snap...** in the pull-down menu brings the
dialogue box on screen. Or keying ddosnap at the command line
brings up the dialogue box – see page 17.

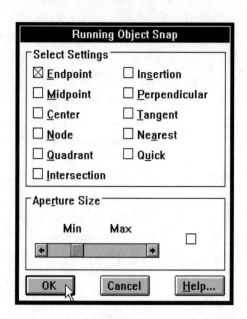

Fig. 2.25 The **Running Object
Snap** dialogue box

Osnaps allow accurate selection of points of entities in a drawing
already on screen. As an example, Fig. 2.26 is a drawing which
consists of three arcs meeting at their endpoints. As each arc was
drawn the Osnap tool **ENDPOINT** was selected from the toolbox.

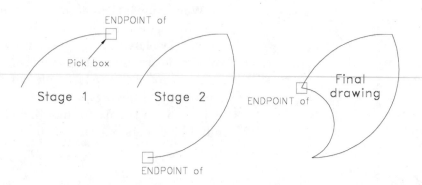

Fig. 2.26 The **ENDPOINT**
Osnap pick box

Any endpoint of an entity within the area of the Osnap pick box is chosen as the required endpoint. Fig. 2.26 was constructed as follows:

Command: *enter* a (for Arc) *right-click*
ARC Center/<start point>: *left-click* at a suitable point
Center/End/<Second point>: *left-click* at a suitable point
End point: *left-click* at a suitable point
Command: *right-click* (to bring back the Arc prompts)
ARC Center/<start point>: *left-click* on the **ENDPOINT** tool in the toolbox. An Osnap pick box appears at the cursor
ENDPOINT of *left-click* on the end of the first arc. An Osnap pick box appears; move it over the end of the first arc and *left-click*

The second arc will now start at exactly the end of the first. Continue in this manner to complete the drawing.

Notes

1. As can be seen in Fig. 2.25, Osnaps are available for: Endpoints, Midpoints, Centres (of circles), Nodes (points), Quadrants (of circles), Intersections (of any crossing entities), Insertion (to the insertion point of an insert), Perpendiculars (perpendicular to an entity), Tangents (to arcs and circles), Nearest (to an entity), Quick (the nearest point to be found). Examples shown in Fig. 2.27;

Fig. 2.27 Examples of **Osnaps**. Each example shows a line to an Osnap point

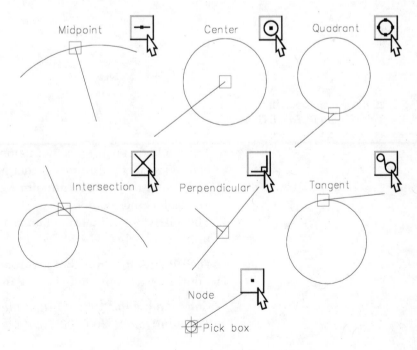

2. When an Osnap is active – check box checked in the **Running Object Snap** dialogue box, a pick box – size set by **Aperture Size** in the dialogue box – appears at the cursor when any command is active;

3. Osnaps can be set at the command line by keying osnap, the command line then shows:

Command: *enter* osnap *right-click*
Object snap modes: *enter* end (for endpoint) or mid (for midpoint) or cen (for centre point) or other abbreviations *right-click*
Command:

and the osnap is set. Other abbreviations are **qua**, **int**, **nea**, **per**, **tan**, **nod** and **ins** for quadrant, intersect, nearest, perpendicular, tangent, node and insert.

An example of the value of Osnaps is given in Fig. 2.28. This shows an example of three features

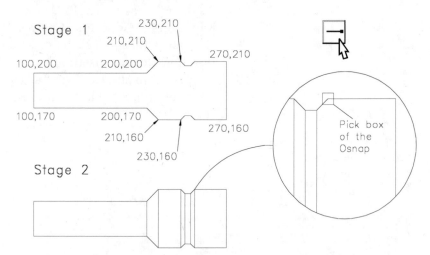

Fig. 2.28 An example of the use of the Osnap **ENDPOINT**

1. The method of using a combination of both **relative** and **absolute** coordinate methods for constructing an outline.
2. The use of the Osnap **Endpoint** to add lines from points on the outline to other points.
3. The relative coordinate method of drawing lines at angle using < to prefix the angle is also shown in this example.

The **ENDPOINT** tool from the toolbox is included with the illustration. The outline was constructed using the **LINE** tool as follows:

Command: *enter* 100,200 *right-click*
To point: *enter* 200,200 *right-click* – then at each **To point:**

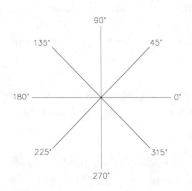

Fig. 2.29 The angles for absolute coordinate entry

prompt in the sequence: 210,210; 230,210; @5<315; @5,0; @5,<45; 270,160 *right-click right-click* (Yes – twice)
Command: *enter* 100,200 *right-click*
To point: *enter* 100,170 *right-click* – then at each **To point:** prompt in the sequence: 200,170; 210,160; 230,160; @5<45; @5,0; @5<315; 270,160 *right-click right-click*
Command:

Notes

1. The double *right-click* at the end of a sequence of coordinate number entries takes the command line back to the **Command:** prompt.
2. When using the **relative** coordinate method of drawing lines at angles, the full 360° notation is used in an anti-clockwise direction commencing from 0° as shown in Fig. 2.29.
3. Although Osnaps are easily set from the **Running Object Snap** dialogue box, or from the command line, personally I find it easier and quicker to select the osnaps as required from the toolbox. In both Figures 2.27 and 2.28, the icons for the Osnaps from the toolbox have been included.

Some keyboard shortcuts

All commands (tools) in AutoCAD LT can be keyed at the keyboard in full or as abbreviations. The abbreviations are listed in the Appendix. Other keyboard shortcuts which will help to speed up working with the software are:

F1   Brings the **Help window** on screen.
F2   Toggles between the AutoCAD graphics window and the AutoCAD LT text window. This will show all the commands called and all entries made at the command line since opening AutoCAD LT.
F5   Toggles the **Isoplanes**. More about these in Chapter 11.
F6   Toggles **Coords** on/off – If off, the coordinate numbers in the coordinate window in the toolbar do not change as the cursor is moved by the mouse.
F7   Toggles **Grid** on/off. If off grid dots do not show.
F8   Toggles **Ortho** on/off. If **Ortho** is on, the construction of entities can only take place along vertical or horizontal axes – a useful feature for some purposes.
F9   Toggles **Snap** on/off.
F10 Toggles menu names in the menu bar on/off. The right and

left arrow keys of the keyboard can then be used to move along the line of menu name. As a name is selected in highlights pressing the *Return* (also named *Enter)* key brings down the menu of the name which is highlighted.

Ctrl/E Press the key marked **Ctrl** and the letter E key toggles the Isoplane – compare with **F5**.

Ctrl/O Toggles **Ortho**.

Ctrl/D Toggles **Coords** between showing absolute coordinate numbers and relative coordinate numbers in the coordinate numbers window.

Ctrl/G Toggles **Grid**.

Ctrl/C Cancels the last entry at the keyboard. Very useful if you have made an error in selecting a tool (command).

Ctrl/B Toggles **Snap**.

Zoom

Left-click on **View** in the menu bar and the **View** pull-down menu appears – Fig. 2.30. *Left-click* on **Zoom** in the menu and the **Zoom** sub-menu appears. This shows the forms of **zoom** available in AutoCAD LT:

All All the area within the **Limits** of the graphics area appears.
Center The point selected with a *left-click* becomes the centre of the graphics area.

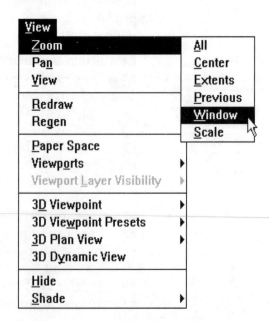

Fig. 2.30 The **View pull-down menu with the** Zoom sub menu

Extents The drawing zooms out to the full extent of the graphics area.

Previous The zoom previously on screen is recalled.

Fig. 2.31 The drawing before **Zoom**

Fig. 2.32 The drawing after **Zoom Extents**

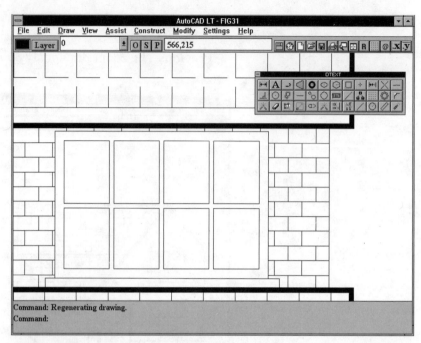

Fig. 2.33 The drawing after a
Zoom Window

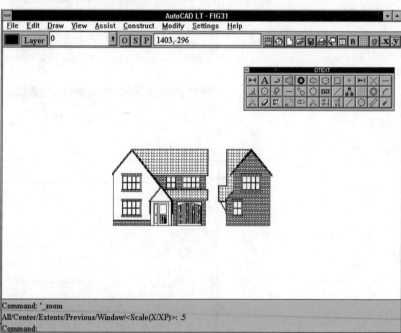

Fig. 2.34 The drawing after a
Zoom to **Scale** 0.5

Window Part of the drawing can be placed in a window chosen
by the operator.

Scale The drawing reduces or enlarges to the scale figure entered
at the keyboard.

Figures 2.31 to 2.34 show the results of the different prompts associated with **Zoom**.

The Aerial View Window

Fig. 2.35 The **Aerial View** icon from the toolbox

Left-click on the **Aerial View** icon in the toolbar (Fig. 2.35). The window appears within the AutoCAD LT graphics window. As can be seen in Fig. 2.36, the full drawing being constructed in the graphics area shows in the **Aerial View** window. The **Aerial View** also shows an area within a window zoom within a black outline.

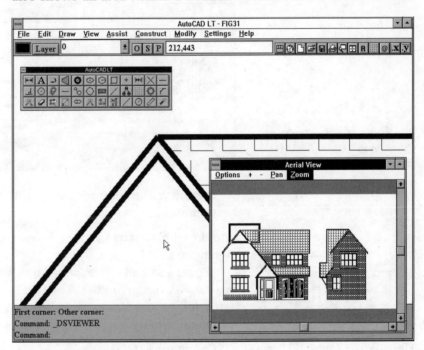

Fig. 2.36 The **Aerial View** window showing a window zoomed from the drawing

The Pan command

This command allows the operator to move around a large drawing to work within part of it. If used in conjunction with the **Aerial View** window, that part of the drawing showing in the AutoCAD LT graphics area is outlined within the full drawing in the **Aerial View**. Using our drawing of a building, Fig. 2.37 shows the result of a **Pan** in both the AutoCAD LT graphics and in the **Aerial View** windows. **Pan** can be called by any of the four methods outlined on p. 23, but probably the easiest method is to enter a p (for Pan) at the command line:

Command: *enter* p *right-click*
PAN Displacement: *pick* a point in the graphics area

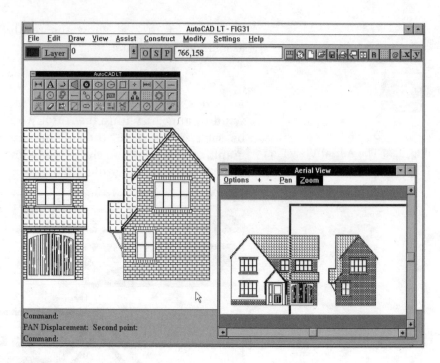

Fig. 2.37 A **Pan** displacement showing in both AutoCAD LT and **Aerial View** windows

Second point: *Pick* another point
Command:

and the whole drawing on screen moves by the distance between the two points.

    Zoom and **Pan** can be called by a *left-click* on their icons, which are usually in the toolbar. The two icons are shown in Fig. 2.38. A *left-click* on the **Zoom** icon brings up the zoom prompts at the command line:

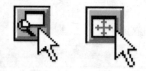

Fig. 2.38 The **Zoom** and **Pan** icons from the toolbar

Command: ZOOM
All/Center/Extents/Previous/Window/<Scale(X/XP)>: *enter* w (for
    Window) *right-click*
First corner: *left-click* at one corner of zoom window on screen
Other corner: *left-click* at other corner of required zoom window
Command: the graphics area changes to the selected area of zoom

Help

An extensive help system can be obtained in AutoCAD LT. When using any tool (command) pressing the **F1** key of the keyboard brings up a window showing help text describing how to use the tool. The window includes (Fig. 2.39):

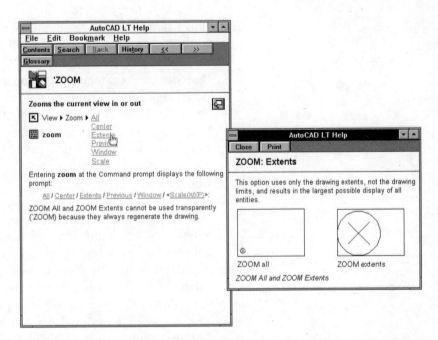

Fig. 2.39 The **Zoom** help window

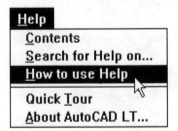

Fig. 2.40 The **Help** pull-down menu

1. A series of buttons along its top edge, the selection of which allows the operator to select Help for other items.
2. A series of help windows for each of the prompts – selected from the text in green – the Help for **Extents** has been selected (pointing finger cursor).
3. The icon for the item the help window covers.
4. Details of the prompts which appear at the command line.

Help can also be called by entering help at the command line or by a *left-click* on **Help** in the menu bar followed by a *left-click* on an item in the pull-down menu which appears – Fig. 2.40.

Revision notes

1. Each feature drawn on a CAD screen is known as an **entity** or as an **object**. Thus each line, circle, arc etc. is an entity (or object). Later in this book it will be seen that some groups of entities (blocks) can be treated as if they were entities.
2. Are you working with **Short** or **Full** menus? It depends on whether you wish to operate by selecting icons, entering the names and commands or their abbreviations at the command line, or wish to select from pull-down menus.
3. All tools (commands) in AutoCAD LT have an abbreviation – see the Appendix in which a complete list of all abbreviations is given.

4. Check that you know the names of the various parts of a dialogue box – Fig. 2.5. This knowledge will be of value when the parts are referred to in later pages.

5. Dialogue boxes can be brought on screen by selection from pull-down menus or by entering a dd call – page 16.

6. AutoCAD LT works with a coordinate system in which any point in the graphics area can be referred to in terms of x,y coordinate numbers. It will be seen later in Chapter 13 that a third coordinate z is available for 3D constructions, but only on drawings imported from AutoCAD.

7. There are four methods of calling commands – selection from pull-down menus, selection of icons from the toolbox or toolbar, entering a command name at the command line; entering an abbreviation for a command at the command line.

8. Accurate constructions can be achieved by using **absolute** and/or **relative** coordinate points entry, by using **Grid** and/or **Snap** and using **Osnap** for ensuring accurate positioning of ends of entities;

9. The keyboard function keys can be used as toggles between features being on or off. **F1** (Help); **F2** (text window); **F5** (Isoplanes); **F6** (Coords); **F7** (Grid); **F8** (Ortho); **F9** (Snap); **F10** (menu names).

10. **Ctrl/C** cancels a command.

11. Use **Zoom** frequently to examine or construct in enlarged parts of a drawing.

12. **Help** by pressing **F1** is associated with the current command.

Exercises

1. Experiment with **Full** and **Short** menus – *left-click* on **Settings** followed by a *left-click* on either **Short Menu** or **Full Menu**, whichever is showing at the time.

2. In the **Drawing Aids** dialogue box set **Snap** and **Grid** to different settings.

3. Experiment with dragging the toolbox or dialogue box to another part of the screen.

4. Examine the Coordinates window in the toolbar as the cursors are moved around the screen under mouse control. Press keys **Ctrl/D** and note what changes take place in the coordinate numbers window as the mouse is moved. Press **Ctrl/D** a second time.

5. Experiment with the function keys and note what happens.

6. Draw any lines, circles and arcs on the screen. First select tool icons from the tool box, then select tool names from the **Draw** pull-down menu, then by entering the tool names at the command line and also their abbreviations – l (Line), c (Circle), a (Arc).

7. Experiment with the **Osnaps**. First by setting them in the **Running Object Snap** dialogue box, then by selecting each one as required from the toolbox.

8. Fig. 2.41. Construct the outline – absolute coordinates method.

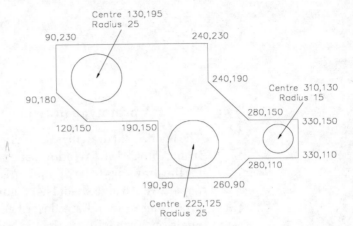

Fig. 2.41 Exercise 8

9. Fig. 2.42. Construct the outline – absolute coordinate method.

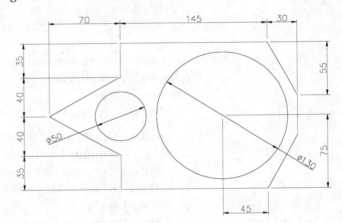

Fig. 2.42 Exercise 9

10. Using any method you think suitable construct the drawing Fig. 2.43.

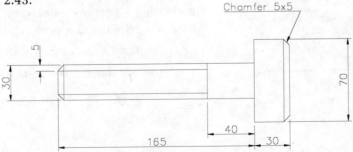

Fig. 2.43 Exercise 10

CHAPTER 3

2D Drawing commands

A prototype drawing

The majority of drawings throughout this book have been constructed in an AutoCAD LT window set up with a prototype drawing suitable for the drawings to be plotted full size on an A3 size sheet of drawing paper. An A3 size sheet is 420 mm by 297 mm. The settings for this prototype drawing are described below. These settings are those made on my machine – the file holding these settings being saved as the default prototype ISO file **acltiso.dwg**. The reader is warned to only save his or her own prototype drawing file to this name if he or she is the sole user of the computer in use. If others are using the computer or if it is on a network, it is advisable to save the file to a filename such as one's initials or Christian name – for example **rgb.dwg** or **ronald.dwg** for an operator whose name is Ronald Graham Brown.

The settings involve:

1. Setting graphics area **Limits**.
2. Setting the number of figures after the decimal point of coordinate numbers etc. – the **Units** setting.
3. Settings **Drawing Aids** – **Snap**, **Grid**, **Ortho** and **Blips**.
4. Setting **Layers**.
5. Setting **Dimension Styles**.
6. Including a title block and borders if required.
7. Whether **Grips** are required or not.
8. Setting a **Text Style** or styles.
9. Saving the file as a prototype drawing file.

My prototype file was set up in the following manner. Others may wish to vary these settings as necessary.

Limits

At the command line:

> **Command:** *enter* limits *right-click*
> **ON/OFF/<Lower left corner><0,0>:** *right-click* (accepts 0,0)
> **Upper right corner:<12,9>:** *enter* 420,297 *right-click*
> **Command:** *enter* z (for Zoom)
> **All/Center/Extents/Previous/Window/<Scale(X/XP)>:** *enter* a (for
>   All) *right-click*
> **Regenerating drawing.**
> **Command:**

Without Zoom All, the limits will remain at the settings already set.

Units

Either *left-click* on **Settings** in the menu bar, followed by a *left-click* on **Units Style...** in the pull-down menu, or *enter* ddunits at the command line. The **Units Control** dialogue box (Fig. 3.1) appears. *Left-click* in the small circle to the left of **Decimal** in the **Units** column, followed by a *left-click* in the **Precision** box. This brings down a pop-up list. In the pop-up list, *left-click* on **0**. This sets the number of figures after a decimal point to none. *Left-click* on the **OK** button of the dialogue box.

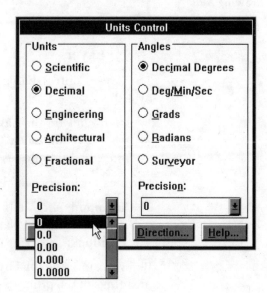

Fig. 3.1 The **Units Control** dialogue box

Drawing Aids

Either *left-click* on **Drawing Aids...** in the **Settings** pull-down menu, or *enter* ddrmodes at the command line. The **Drawing Aids** dialogue box appears (Fig. 3.2). Check that **Solid Fill**, **Highlight**, **Snap** and **Grid** are set on (diagonals in check boxes). *Enter* 5 in the **X Spacing** box of **Snap**. The **Y Spacing** automatically also sets to 5. In a similar manner set the **Grid** spacings to 10. If you prefer **Blips** to show (small crosses at each selected point in the AutoCAD LT graphics area) when constructing drawings, set **Blips** on. Personally I prefer **Blips** to be off.

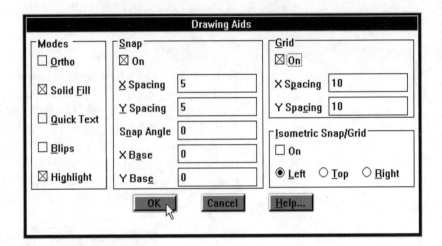

Fig. 3.2 The **Drawing Aids**
dialogue box

Layers

The **Layer Control** dialogue box (Fig. 3.3) can be brought onto screen by either:

A *left-click* on the **Layer** button in the menu bar, or;
A *left-click* on **Layer Control...** in the **Settings** dialogue box, or;
Entering ddlmodes as the command line:

Settings for layers can also be made at the command line by:

Command: *enter* la (for Layer) *right-click*
LAYER ?/Make/Set/New/ON/OFF/Color/Ltype/Freeze/Thaw/LOck/
   Unlock:

Before examining the **Layer Control** dialogue box, let us look at the meanings of the prompts when Layer is called at the command line:

?   followed by 2 *right-clicks* brings up a text window showing the layers already set.

M   and a set of prompts requesting the name of the layer to be made appears at the command line.

S   and a set of prompts appears requesting the name of the layer to be set as current layer.

N   and a set of prompts appears requesting the name of the new layer to be included in the layer list.

ON   and a set of prompts appears requesting the name of the layer which had previously been off to be turned back on.

OFF   and a set of prompts appears requesting the name of the layer(s) to be turned off. A layer which is off cannot be worked on.

C   and another set of prompts appears requesting the colour to be used for entities in a named layer.

L   and a set of prompts appears requesting the linetype to be set for the current layer.

F   and a set of prompts appears requesting the name of the layer to be frozen. A frozen layer cannot be used in any way and whatever is on its surface never appears on screen.

T   and a set of prompts appears requesting the name of the layer previously frozen to be thawed.

LO   and a set of prompts appears requesting the name of the layer to be locked. Constructions on a **LOcked** layer cannot be acted upon by any of the Modify or Construct commands, although constructions can be added to a locked layer.

U   and set of prompts appears requesting the name of the layer to be unlocked.

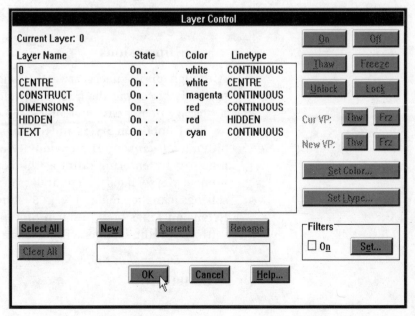

Fig. 3.3 The **Layer Control** dialogue box

Any of these settings can be made in the **Layer Control** dialogue box by using the buttons – **On**, **Off**, **Thaw**, **Freeze**, **Unlock**, **Lock**, **New**, **Current**, **Set Color** and **Set Ltype**.

Before a **Linetype** can be set for a layer, the necessary line types must first be loaded from the **Settings** pull-down menu by a *left-click* on **Linetype Style**, followed by another on **Load** in the **Linetype Style** sub-menu. Then, at the command line:

> **Command:**_linetype
> **?/Create/Load/Set:_load**
> **Linetype(s) to load:** *enter* centre, hidden *right-click*

and the **Select Linetype File** dialogue box appears. All that is required is a *left-click* on the **OK** button of this box to load the required linetype.

It is advisable to also select **Linetype Scale** from the same sub-menu and set the scale to 0.5 from the prompts appearing at the command line.

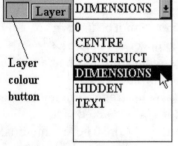

Layer colour button

Fig. 3.4 The pop-up list appearing when the Layer Name button in the toolbar is selected

Once the linetypes and their scale have been loaded the settings for layers can be made in the **Layer Control** dialogue box, using the appropriate buttons as required. The settings shown in Fig. 3.3 are those set for my computer. The reader may wish to have different settings.

The current layer can be set, either from the **Layer Control** dialogue box, or more quickly, by a *left-click* in the Layer name window in the toolbar, followed by another *left-click* on the layer name in the pop-up list which appears. The colour for the layer then appears in the Layer Colour button in the toolbar – Fig. 3.4.

Dimensions

Although it is not necessary at this stage to set **Dimension Styles**, the methods of setting them is briefly described here. It will become necessary in any case at a later stage (Chapter 8).

The **Dimension Styles and Settings** dialogue box can be called by either a *left-click* on **Dimension Styles...** in the **Settings** pull-down menu or by *entering* ddim at the command line. This box has a number of associated dialogue boxes in which the various dimensional settings can be made. Fig. 3.5 shows only one of these – the **Extension Lines** box. In our prototype drawing file, the following settings for dimensions will be made:

> *Dimension Style*
> **SIMPLEX**

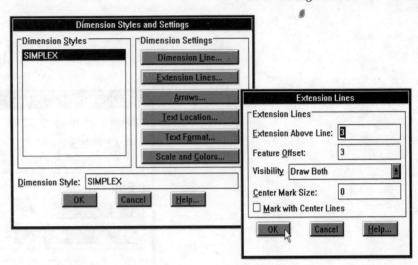

Fig. 3.5 The **Dimensions Styles and Settings** dialogue box, with the **Extension Lines** box selected

Dimension Line box

Force Interior Line check box off
Basic Dimension check box off
Text Gap *enter* 1
Basic Line Increment *enter* 3

Extension Lines box

Extension Above Line *enter* 3
Feature Offset *enter* 3
Visibility from pop-up list **Draw both**
Center Mark Size *enter* 0

Arrows box

Arrow circular check box on
Arrow Size *enter* 4

Text Location box

Text Height *enter* 4
Tolerance Height *enter* 2
Horizontal from pop-up list **Default**
Vertical from pop-up list **Above**
Alignment from pop-up list **Align With Dimension Line**

Scale and Colors box

Feature Scaling *enter* 1
Set all colours to red.

Grips

For the time being turn grips off in the **Grips** dialogue box (Fig. 3.6)

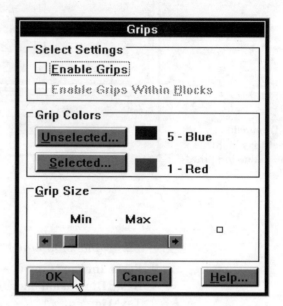

Fig. 3.6 The **Grips** dialogue box showing the **Enable Grips** check box off

Text Style

In the **Select Text Font** dialogue box (Fig. 3.7) *double-left-click* on **Roman Simplex**. A series of prompts appear at the command line. Set the parameters for the font style **Romans** (Simplex) to:

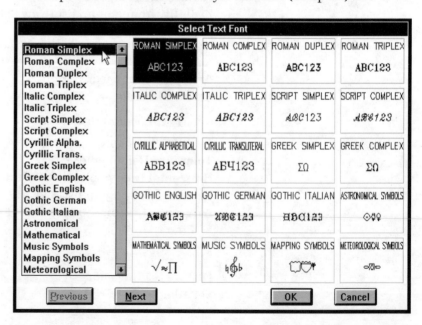

Fig. 3.7 The **Select Text Font** dialogue box

Height: 6; **Width factor:** 1; **Obliquing angle:** 0; **Backwards:** No;
Upside-down: No; **Vertical:** No. The command line then changes to:

ROMANS is now the current text style
Command:

Borders and title box

If required borders and an empty title box can be saved with the
prototype file. This may be a simple layout suitable for students or
beginners learning how to use AutoCAD LT or a more complex
layout suitable for an industrial concern. Examples are given in
Figures 3.8 and 3.9.

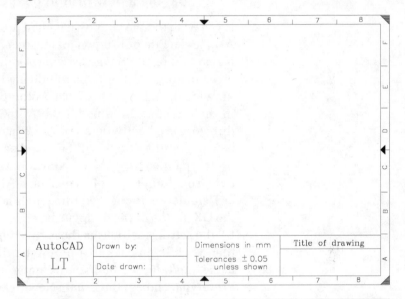

Fig. 3.8 A title block and
borders suitable for use in
industry

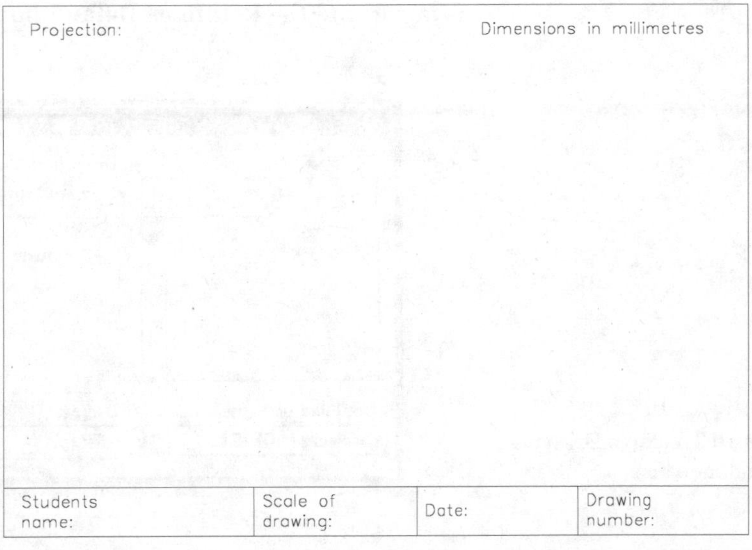

Fig. 3.9 A title block and
borders more suitable for
student use

Saving the prototype drawing file

Take care when saving your prototype drawing to a file on disk. Remember the advice given above – if others are using the computer at which you are working, it is advisable that your prototype drawing file is saved to a name other than the default prototype drawing files. There are two prototype drawing files with the software of AutoCAD LT – *aclt.dwg* and *acltiso.dwg*. When AutoCAD LT is first started up the window that appears is one with the prototype drawing file *aclt.dwg* or *acltiso.dwg* loaded. The start-up prototype file can be changed if required.

Saving a new prototype drawing file

If you wish to save your own named prototype file, *left-click* on **Save As...** in the **File** pull-down menu and *enter* your filename in the **File Name** box of the **Save Drawing As** dialogue box. In the example given in Fig. 3.10, the name **ronald** has been *entered* as the prototype drawing file name. Note that a prototype drawing file must be saved in the directory holding all the AutoCAD LT files – normally the directory is **c:\acltwin**. A *left-click* on the **OK** button of the dialogue box and your settings will be saved as *ronald.dwg*. To use this as a prototype file, *left-click* on **New...** in the **File** pull-down menu and *enter* **ronald** in the **Prototype...** box. Also make sure that the **Retain as Default** box is checked (diagonals across box). Then *left-click* on the **OK** button of the dialogue box. Next time you start up AutoCAD LT the settings will be as those saved in the **ronald.dwg** file. If you then wish to go back to a prototype file with either of the default names *aclt.dwg* or *acltiso.dwg* enter either of these names in the **Prototype...** box in the **Create New Drawing** dialogue box and again make sure the **Retain as Default** box is checked.

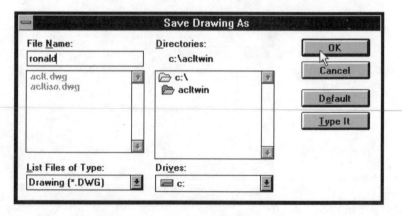

Fig. 3.10 The **Save Drawing As** dialogue box

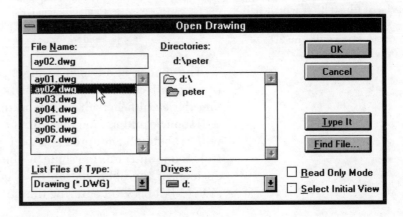

Create New Drawing

Prototype...   ronald

☐ No Prototype
☒ Retain as Default

New Drawing Name...

OK   Cancel

Fig. 3.11 The **Create New Drawing** dialogue box

The AutoCAD drawing file *.dwg

The file ending with the filename extension **.dwg** has been referred to several times in previous pages. When a drawing has been constructed in AutoCAD LT it can be saved to a filename *entered* in **File Name** box of the **Save Drawing As** dialogue box. Without including the extension **.dwg**, the drawing will be saved to the filename and the extension will be automatically added. To open a drawing file *left-click* on **Open...** in the **File** pull-down menu and the **Open Drawing** dialogue box (Fig. 3.12) appears. The required drawing can then be opened either by a *double-left-click* on the required filename in the filename list box, or by a single *left-click* on the name, followed by a *left-click* on the **OK** button of the dialogue box. In Fig. 3.12 the drawing file ay02.dwg has been selected to be opened into the AutoCAD LT graphics window.

Note that drawings saved in AutoCAD LT with the filename extension **.dwg** can be opened in AutoCAD Releases 11 or 12, in AutoCAD for Windows, in AutoSketch for Windows Release 2 and in Generic CADD Release 6.1. This form of drawing file is compatible with these other types of CAD software published by Autodesk.

Open Drawing

File **N**ame:
ay02.dwg

ay01.dwg
ay02.dwg
ay03.dwg
ay04.dwg
ay05.dwg
ay06.dwg
ay07.dwg

Directories:
d:\peter

d:\
peter

OK
Cancel

Type It
Find File...

List Files of **T**ype:
Drawing (*.DWG)

Drives:
d:

☐ **R**ead Only Mode
☐ **S**elect Initial View

Fig. 3.12 The **Open Drawing** dialogue box

Drawing tools

The four methods of calling commands in AutoCAD LT were described on p. 23. A tool or command can be called by selecting a tool icon from the toolbox or from the toolbar, by selection from a pull-down menu, by typing the command or tool name in full at the command line or by typing its abbreviation at the command line. In the following pages describing the construction of entities (objects) in the AutoCAD graphics area, the descriptions will be accompanied by illustrations showing the tool (command) name selected from the relevant pull-down menu, the icon selected from the toolbox and a drawing of the key(s) to be pressed for the tool (command) name abbreviation. As an example the illustration to accompany the **LINE** tool is shown in Fig. 3.13. As is shown in Fig. 3.13, the operator can choose between selection from a pull-down menu, selecting an icon or entering a letter or (in some cases) letters.

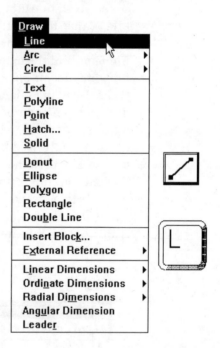

Fig. 3.13 An example of the type of illustration which will appear when describing constructing with the 2D drawing tools

The reader is advised to practise with all three methods and occasionally enter the full tool or command name in order to familiarise him/herself with working with AutoCAD LT. In fact it will soon be understood that a mixture from the three (four) methods will probably be adopted – selecting some from the menus, some from icons and entering some by abbreviations. If the appearance of an icon or the abbreviation for a command is forgotten, one can always fall back on entering the full name.

In describing the use of the tools, it is assumed that the reader will select the tool (command) by using any one of the methods. As explained earlier in this book, when any tool or command is called, prompts appear at the command line. As each tool is described, only these prompts will be given together with the necessary action to produce a construction. Remember the following:

1. **Command:** all command line prompts will appear in **bold** text.
2. The prompt shown in brackets **< >** is the default prompt – the one that will be in operation if no other prompt is called.
3. To call a prompt showing in the command line, enter the capital letters of the prompt.
4. *enter* means type the given letters, words etc. at the keyboard.
5. *left-click* means press the left hand button of the mouse and promptly release it.
6. *right-click* means press the right hand button of the mouse and promptly release it.
7. The two words *tool* and *command* are for all practical purposes interchangeable, but in general, *tool* will be used when a construction is involved and *command* when other operations are involved.

The tool LINE

This has already been described in sufficient detail – pp. 23–9. Lines are drawn in *rubber band* style – as each **To point:** position is *picked* with either a *left-click* at a point in the graphics area or a coordinate position entered at the command line, the line is rubber banded from that point, waiting (as it were) for the next point to be selected. Rubber banding of points continues until either the *Enter* key of the keyboard is pressed or a *right-click* of the mouse is given, when the prompt **To point:** reverts back to **Command:**.

The tool DLINE (double line)

Command: DLINE
Break/Caps/Dragline/Offset/Snap/Width/<start point>:

The meanings of the prompts are shown in Fig. 3.15. Each of the prompts has it own prompt line:

Break: **Dlines at start and end points?OFF/<ON>:**
Caps: **Draw which endcaps? Both/End/None/Start <Auto>:**
Dragline: **Set dragline position to Left/Center/Right/<Center>:**
Snap: **Set snap size or snap On/Off. Size/OFF/<ON>:**
Width: **New DLINE width<10>:**

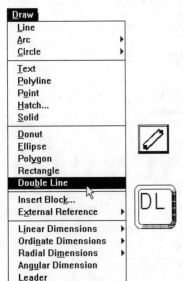

Fig. 3.14 Calling **Double Line**

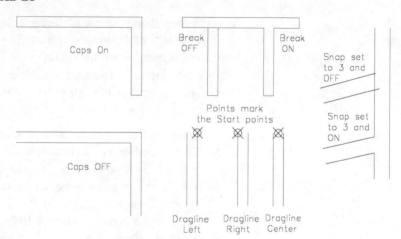

Fig. 3.15 The results of the actions of prompts when using the **DLINE** tool

The tool ARC

Start, Second, End or 3-point

Command: ARC Center/<Start point>: *pick* a point or *enter* coordinates
Center/End?<Second point>: *pick* a point or *enter* coordinates
End point: *pick* a point or *enter* coordinates
Command:

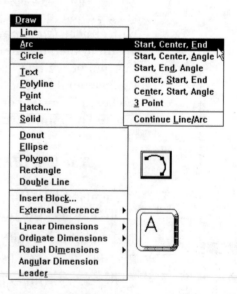

Fig. 3.16 Calling **Arc**

Center, Start, End

Command: ARC Center/<Start point>: *enter* c
(for Center) *right-click*
Center: *pick* a point or *enter* coordinates

Start point: *pick* a point or *enter* coordinates
Angle/<End point>: *pick* a point or *enter* coordinates
Command:

Center, Start, Included angle

Command: ARC Center/<Start point>: *enter* c (for Center)
right-click
Center: *pick* a point or *enter* coordinates
Start point: *pick* a point or *enter* coordinates
Angle/<End point> *enter* a (for Angle) *right-click*
Included angle: *enter* angle figures *right-click*
Command:

Start, End, Included angle

Command: ARC Center/<Start point>: *pick* a point or   *enter*
coordinates
Center/End?<Second point>: *enter* e (for End) *right-click*
End point: *pick* a point or *enter* coordinates
Included angle: *enter* angle figures *right-click*
Command:

Fig. 3.17 Some examples of
arcs

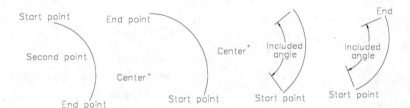

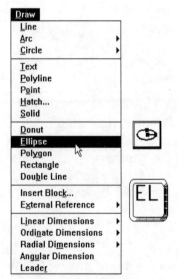

Fig. 3.18 Calling **Ellipse**

The tool CIRCLE

This has already been described in sufficient detail – pp. 24 – 25.

The tool ELLIPSE

An ellipse can be regarded as the outline produced when a circle, viewed from its front, is rotated around one of its diameters. If the rotation is about the circle's horizontal diameter, so its vertical diameter becomes smaller as rotation continues until all that can be seen is the 'edge' of the circle. In the resulting ellipse, the larger diameter is the *major axis* of the ellipse and the smaller diameter, the *minor axis*. See Fig. 3.19.

There are several ways of drawing an ellipse in AutoCAD LT, depending upon whether it is to be based upon its two axes, its centre and its axes or the angle of rotation around its major axis.

Fig. 3.19 The results of the actions of prompts when using the **ELLIPSE** tool

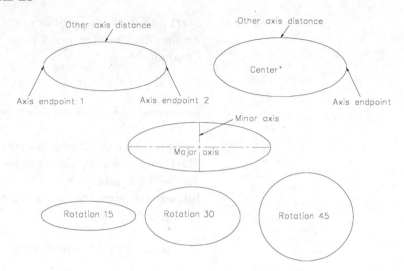

Both axes

Command: ELLIPSE
<Axis endpoint1>/Center *pick* a point or *enter* coordinates
<Axis endpoint 2> *pick* a point or *enter* coordinates
<Other axis distance>/Rotation: *pick* a point or *enter* coordinates
Command:

Centre and two axes

Command: ELLIPSE
<Axis endpoint1>/Center *enter* c (for Center) *right-click*
Center of ellipse: *pick* a point or *enter* coordinates
Axis endpoint: *pick* a point or *enter* coordinates
<Other axis distance>/Rotation: *pick* a point or *enter* coordinates
Command:

Centre, major ellipse and rotation

Command: ELLIPSE
<Axis endpoint1>/Center *enter* c (for Center) *right-click*
Center of ellipse: *pick* a point or *enter* coordinates
Axis endpoint: *pick* a point or *enter* coordinates
<Other axis distance>/Rotation: *enter* r (for Rotation) *right-click*
Rotation about major axis: *enter* angle figures *right-click*
Command:

The tool POLYGON

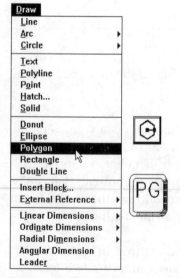

Fig. 3.20 Calling **Polygon**

Only regular polygons can be drawn with the aid of this tool – all sides of equal length and all angles of equal size. The polygon can

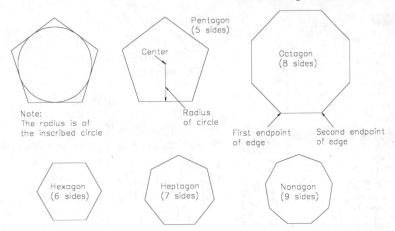

Fig. 3.21 The results of the actions of prompts with the **Polygon** tool

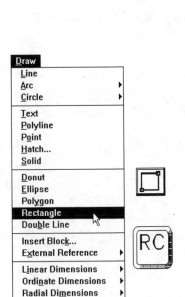

Fig. 3.22 Calling **Rectangle**

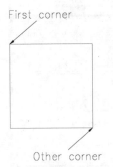

Fig. 3.23 The results of the actions of the prompts in the **Rectangle** tool

be produced with any number of sides, set in response to the first prompt at the command line.

Command: POLYGON Number of sides <4>: *enter* a figure
   right-click

   Polygon based on radius of inscribed circle

Command: POLYGON Number of sides <4>: *enter* 5 *right-click*
Edge/<Center of polygon>: *pick* a point or *enter* coordinates
Radius of circle: *pick* a point or *enter* a figure for the radius
Command:

   Polygon based on edge length

Command: POLYGON Number of sides <4>: *enter* 8 *right-click*
Edge/<Center of polygon>: *enter* e (for Edge) *right-click*
First endpoint of edge: *pick* a point or *enter* coordinates
Second endpoint of edge: *pick* a point or *enter* coordinates
Command:

The tool RECTANGLE

Use this tool to draw rectangles of any size. The lines of the rectangle are polylines (plines), see p. 59. The rectangle can be drawn starting at any corner, but is always drawn with its edges vertically and horizontally. Because rectangles constructed with this tool are plines, the resulting entities are of current pline width. Thus if plines have been drawn with width set to say 2, then rectangles will be drawn with sides of width 2 units.

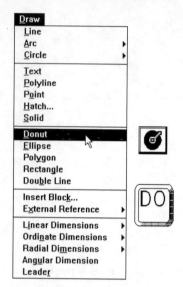

Fig. 3.24 Calling **Donut**

Command: RECTANG
First corner: *pick* a point or *enter* coordinates
Other corner: *pick* a point or *enter* coordinates
Command:

The tool DONUT

When responses to the two prompts of the **Donut** tool, a *ghosted* donut appears at the cursor cross-hairs. The donut can be paced in position as many times as is desired by *picking* points in the Graphics area, or by entering coordinates followed by a *right-click* without recalling the tool. Not until the final *right-click* will the prompts cease.

Command: DONUT
Inside diameter <1>: *enter* a figure or *pick* 2 points on screen
Outside diameter <1>: *enter* a figure or *pick* 2 points on screen
Center of doughnut: *pick* a point or *enter* coordinates followed by
   a *right t-click*
Center of doughnut: *right-click* to finish placing donuts
Command:

The tool POINT

Associated with this tool is the **Point Style** dialogue box. First select the style of point required from the **Point Style** dialogue box – called from the **Settings** pull-down menu. Then:

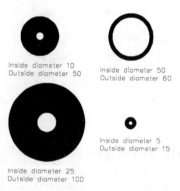

Inside diameter 10
Outside diameter 50

Inside diameter 50
Outside diameter 60

Inside diameter 5
Outside diameter 15

Inside diameter 25
Outside diameter 100

Fig. 3.25 The results of the actions of the prompts of the **Donut** tool

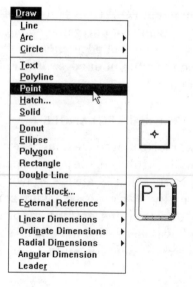

Fig. 3.26 Calling **Point** and the **Point Style** dialogue box

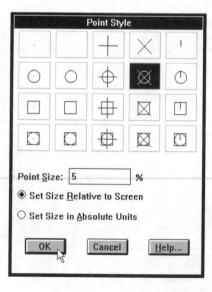

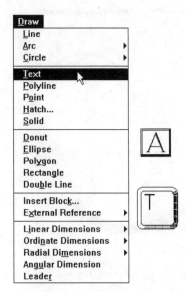

Fig. 3.27 Calling **TEXT**

Command:
POINT Point: *pick* a position on screen or *enter* coordinates
Command:

The tool TEXT

More about this tool in Chapter 6. Text is sufficiently important in technical drawings to require a number of pages of explanation for using this tool. For the time being, it should be noted that if the **Text** tool is called by selection from the **Draw** pull-down menu, by selecting the Text tool icon or by entering t (or dt), it is *dynamic text* which will appear in the graphics area. The text appears on screen as it is keyed at the keyboard. If however the full tool name **text** is entered at the keyboard, the text does not appear on screen until either a *right-click* or the *enter* key of the keyboard is pressed. However when any one of the three methods of calling the tool shown in Fig. 3.27 is used, a *right-click* does not act as with other tools. Instead of a *right-click* the *enter* key must be pressed.

> **Command: DTEXT Justify/Style/<Start point>:** *pick* a point or
> *enter* coordinates
> **Rotation angle <0>:** *right-click* (to accept the angle 0)
> **Text:** *enter* the required text at the keyboard, press the *enter* key
> **Text:** press the *enter* key
> **Command:**

Rows of text can be placed on screen, each one below the previous row by entering text at each **Text:** prompt. When the final line has been placed pressing *Enter* at the prompt closes the series of prompts.

The tool PLINE

The **Pline** allows lines (polylines) to be drawn to any desired width. In addition, plines can also be drawn in curves. Associated with the **Pline** tool is the tool (command) **Edit polyline** (Pedit), which allows the editing of polylines once they have been drawn. Plines can be drawn with **Solid Fill** on or off (set in **Drawing Aids** dialogue box). The following series of prompts shows how a variety of plines can be drawn. Fig. 3.29 gives a number of examples of plines.

> **Command: PLINE**
> **From point:** *pick* point on screen or *enter* coordinates
> **Arc/Close/Halfwidth/Length/Width/<Endpoint of line>:** *enter* w
> (for Width) *right-click*
> **Starting width <0>:** *right-click* to accept or *enter* a figure
> **Ending width <0>:** *right-click* to accept or *enter* a figure

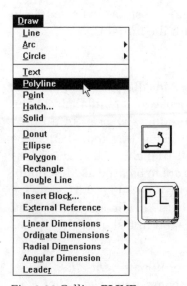

Fig. 3.28 Calling **PLINE**

Fig. 3.29 A variety of plines

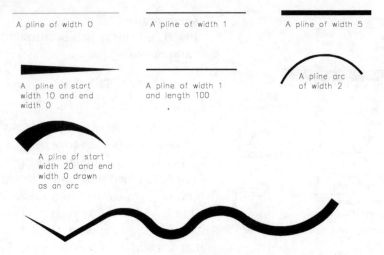

Arc/Close/Halfwidth/Length/Width/<Endpoint of line>: *enter* a
  (for Arc) *right-click*
<Endpoint of arc>: *enter* s (for Second) *right-click*
Second point: *pick* a point or *enter* coordinates
End point: *pick* a point or *enter* coordinates
<Endpoint of arc>: *enter* l (for Length)
Arc/Close/Halfwidth/Length/Width/<Endpoint of line>:

Another series of prompts will appear after a second **Endpoint of
arc:** prompt. These prompts relate to the arc about to be drawn:

Angle/CEnter/CLose/Direction/Halfwidth/Length/Radius/Second
  point/Undo/Width/<Endpoint of arc>:

Note the first two letters of **CEnter** and **CLose** in this example to
differentiate between two prompts with the initial **C**.

The tool SOLID

With **Solid Fill** set ON in the **Drawing Aids** dialogue box, this tool
allows the drawing of a solid filled area between points selected on
screen. If **Solid Fill** is OFF the tool produces a series of unfilled
triangles in the graphics area. When using this tool it must be
understood that the solid areas are all triangles. This determines
which of each of the triangles' corners are to be used as **First point**,
Second point, **Third point** and **Fourth point**. Fig. 3.31 shows a
number of solid filled areas constructed with the aid of the **Solid**
tool. When the tool is called the command line shows:

Command: SOLID
First point: *pick* a point or *enter* coordinates *right-click*
Second point: *pick* a point or *enter* coordinates *right-click*

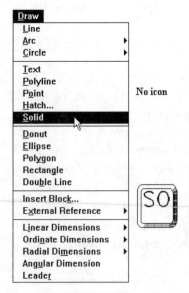

No icon

Fig. 3.30 Calling **Solid**

Third point: *pick* a point or *enter* coordinates *right-click*
Fourth point: *pick* a point or *enter* coordinates *right-click*
Third point: *pick* a point or *enter* coordinates *right-click*
Fourth point: *pick* a point or *enter* coordinates *right-click*
Third point: *right-click* to complete the solid
Command:

Note that until a *right-click* is given at the prompt **Third point:** the prompt **Fourth point:** will continue reappearing after **Third point:** If **Solid Fill** is OFF the outline triangles of the area show clearly – Fig. 3.31.

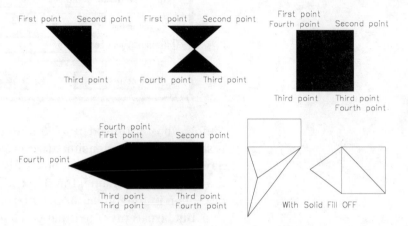

Fig. 3.31 The action of the tool **Solid**

Saving your drawings to file

Like any other machine, computers are fallible. If, for example, the electric supply is suddenly cut off – fuse going, thunderstorm interfering with the electric supply or any other cause, the drawing you have been working on will be lost – all of it unless you have saved your work at frequent intervals. The best way of dealing with this problem is to get into the habit of saving your work at frequent intervals – say every fifteen minutes or so. You can set AutoCAD LT to automatically save your work at set intervals, but this can cause difficulties at times when working on a drawing which you do not wish to save to the current filename. Fig. 3.32 shows how **Automatic Save** is set up. From the **File** pull-down menu select **Preferences...** and in the **Preferences** dialogue box check the **Automatic Save Every** box and set the time as desired to the required number of minutes. The file is saved to the filename you have chosen for your drawing file.

To save a drawing to file, select **Save As...** from the **File** pull-down menu and *enter* a suitable filename in the **File Name** box of the

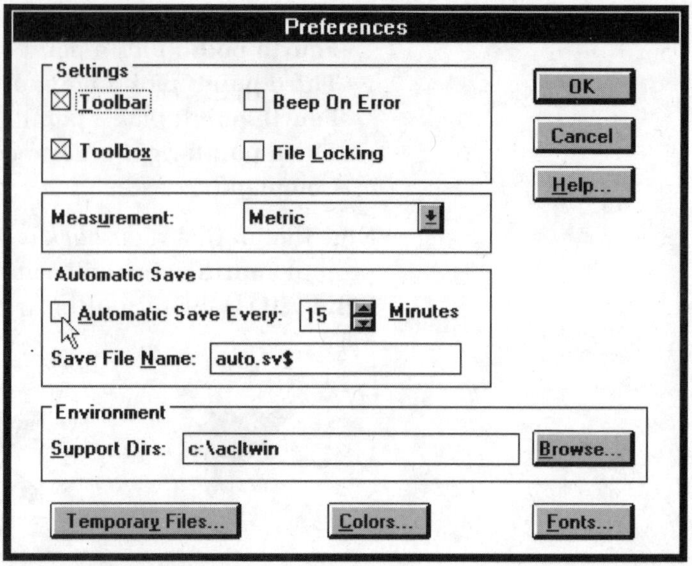

Fig. 3.32 **Automatic Save** settings in the **preferences** dialogue box

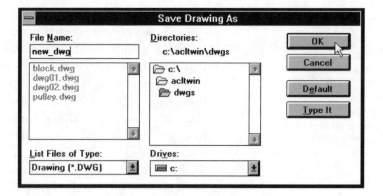

dialogue box, followed by a *left-click* on the **OK** button. The drawing is saved with the extension **.dwg** as can be seen in the list box of the **Save Drawing As** dialogue box – Fig. 3.33. Once you have saved a drawing to its filename, the file can be saved by a *left-click* on the **Save** icon in the toolbar or by *entering* sa (or save) at the command line. But be careful either that you have saved the file already to the correct filename or that you have given the drawing a **New Drawing Name** in the **Create New Drawing** dialogue box.

Fig. 3.33 The **Save As** dialogue box

Fig. 3.34 The **Save** tool icon in the toolbar

Questions

1. When is it inadvisable to save your own prototype drawing to the filename acltiso?
2. What is the file extension for an AutoCAD drawing file?

3. How is a prototype drawing file saved? With which other CAD software programmes is the AutoCAD drawing file compatible?
4. How many methods of calling tools or commands are there in AutoCAD LT?
5. What are the differences between the actions of **LINE** and **PLINE**?
6. What are the names given to the two axes of an ellipse?
7. Why is it that you may draw a rectangle with the tool **RECTANGLE** and find that it is made up of thick lines?
8. What is a regular polygon?
9. How is the style of a point set?
10. What is the difference between calling the text tool by selecting the **TEXT** icon and entering text at the command line?

Exercises

1. Copy the text in Fig. 3.35 after setting each text style in the **Text Style** dialogue box.

AutoCAD LT
Roman Complex 15 high

My name is ?.???????
Roman Duplex 20 high

Italic Complex 18 high

Gothic English 14 high

Roman Simplex 22 high

Fig. 3.35 Exercise 1

2.   Fig. 3.36. Using the **LINE** tool and working with the relative coordinates method construct the four drawings.

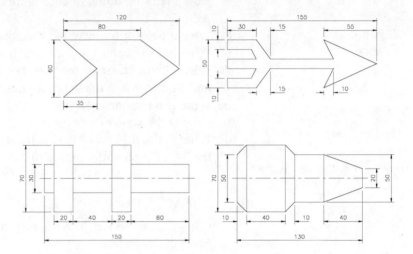

Fig. 3.36 Exercise 2

3.   Fig. 3.37. Using **CIRCLE**, **ARC** and **LINE** tools copy the four drawings. Use the **Osnap** tangent to draw lines between the circles of drawing 2.

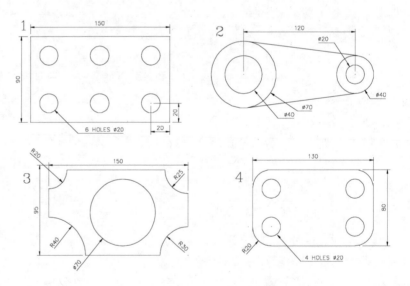

Fig. 3.37 Exercise 3

4.   Using Fig. 3.38 as an example and with the tools **DLINE** and **TEXT** (Romand Simplex 6 high) construct a sketch map of some roads near where you live.

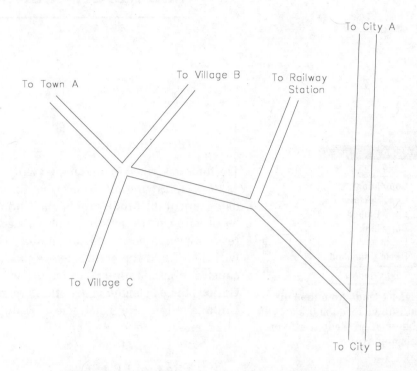

Fig. 3.38 Exercise 4

5.   Fig. 3.39. Copy the given drawings with the aid of the tools **PLINE**, **DONUT** and **SOLID**.

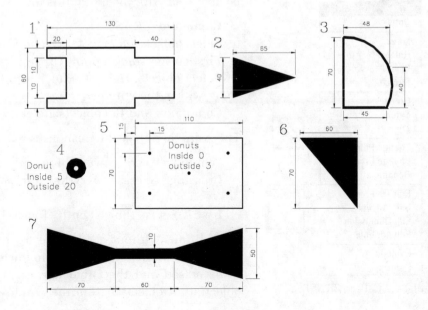

Fig. 3.39 Exercise 5

CHAPTER 4

The Modify commands

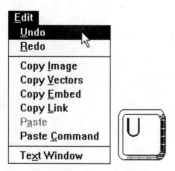

Fig. 4.1 **Undo** from the **Edit** pull-down menu and its abbreviation. **Redo** is also in this menu

Introduction

The tools described in this chapter will probably be used as frequently as the 2D drawing tools described in the previous chapter. When using any of the **Modify** tools, the **Undo** tool (Fig. 4.1) may prove to be of value if the modification carried out does not produce the results wished because **Undo** undoes the last action. If repeated it will then undo the action before that and so on until a complete construction is undone. If a feature which has been acted upon by **Undo** is to be brought back to the screen use **Redo**, but only the last **Undo** is redone. Repeated use of **Redo** will have no further effect. The abbreviation for **Redo** is **RE**.

The tool ERASE

If a mistake is made during a construction, erasure of the error can be achieved with the aid of this tool. When the tool is selected:

> **Command: ERASE**
> **Select objects:** *enter* w (for Window) or c (for Crossing) *right-click*
> **First corner:** *pick* a point **Other corner:** *pick* a point
> **Select objects:** *right-click* to accept the objects which highlight within the window
> **Command:** and the objects are erased

There are three possible responses to the first **Select objects::**

> Window: To erase everything within a window.
> Crossing: To erase everything crossed by the lines of a crossing window.
> Last: To erase the last entity (object) drawn.

In addition, without a response to the first **Select objects:**, if a window **First corner** is selected to the left and outside the object(s) to be erased and the **Other corner** to the right and outside the object(s) all objects *within* the window will be erased. If a **First**

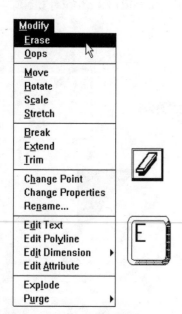

Fig. 4.2 Calling **ERASE**

Fig. 4.3 Some of the results of using the **Erase** tool

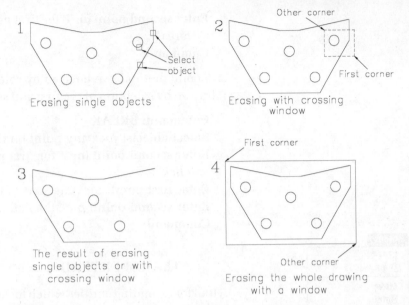

corner is selected to the right of the object(s) and the **Other corner** to the left of the object(s) all objects *crossed* by the lines of the window will be erased.

The tool BREAK

Parts of entities can be erased with the aid of **Break**. When using the tool on circular parts – arcs or circles – remember that the normal direction of working in AutoCAD LT is *anti-clockwise* (or counter clockwise – ccw). See the examples in Fig. 4.5.

Call the tool and the command line changes to:

Command: BREAK
Select objects: *pick* the start of the break area on the entity

Fig. 4.4 Calling **Break**

Fig. 4.5 Some examples of the results of using the **Break** tool

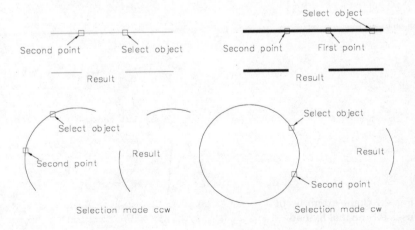

Enter second point (or F for first point): *pick* the end of the break
area
Command:

A second method can be used by selecting the entity to be broken,
followed by selection of the first and second points of the break area:

Command: BREAK
Select objects: *pick* any point on the entity
Enter second point (or F for first point): *enter* f (for First) *right-click*
Enter first point: *pick* the start of the break area on the entity
Enter second point: *pick* the end of the break area
Command:

The tool EXTEND

A tool for extending entities which for some reason are not sufficiently
long.

Command: EXTEND
Select boundary edge(s)... *pick* object
Select objects: *right-click* **1 found.**
Select objects: *right-click*
<Select object to extend>/Undo: *pick* object to be extended
Command:

Fig. 4.7 shows examples of the extension of entities up to boundary
lines. In some circumstances, it may be worth while to draw a

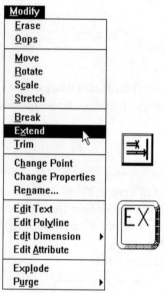

Fig. 4.6 Calling **Extend**

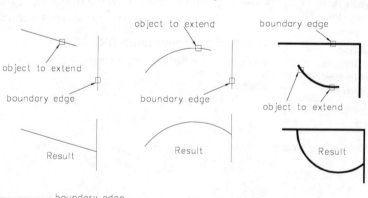

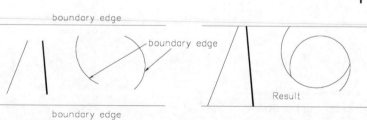

Fig. 4.7 Some examples of
uses for the tool **Extend**

temporary boundary line if one wishes to extend entities by a certain amount, then erase the temporary boundary line when the extension has been completed.

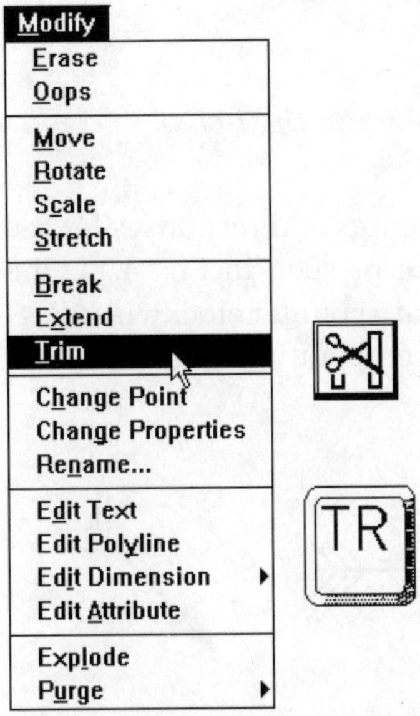

The tool TRIM

A tool for modifying entities that have been drawn beyond other entities and require to be trimmed back. Fig. 4.9 shows some examples of entities which have been constructed beyond boundaries, which have been trimmed back with the aid of the tool.

The sequence of prompts when the command is called follow the pattern:

Command: TRIM
Select cutting edge(s)...
Select objects: *pick* **1 found**
Select objects: *right-click*
<Select objects to trim>/Undo: *pick*
<Select objects to trim>/Undo: *pick*
<Select objects to trim>/Undo: *pick*
<Select objects to trim>/Undo: *right-click*
Command:

Note: Under suitable circumstances, a group of entities can be trimmed by using the f (for crossing fence) response, enabling trimming of a row of entities within a crossing window. See note later in this chapter.

Fig. 4.8 Calling **Trim**

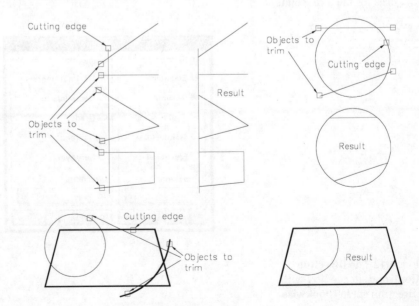

Fig. 4.9 Some examples of the uses for **Trim**

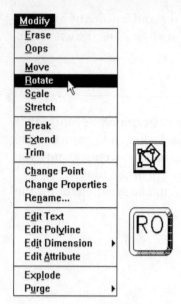

Fig. 4.10 Calling **Rotate**

The tool ROTATE

Command: ROTATE
Select objects: *enter* w (for Window) *right-click*
First corner: *pick* **Other corner:** *pick* **10 found.**
Select objects: *right-click*
Base point: *pick* a suitable point
<Rotation angle>/Reference: *enter* a figure *right-click*
Command:

The example given above shows the prompts and responses for the 45° rotation shown in Fig. 4.11. As can be seen in Fig. 4.11, the rotations follow the AutoCAD LT rule that a counter clockwise (ccw) rotation is performed when the tool is in operation.

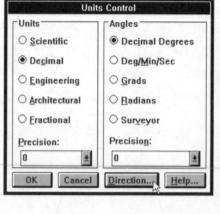

Fig. 4.11 Some examples of the uses for the tool **Rotate**

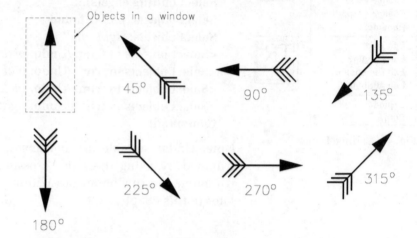

Fig. 4.12 The **Direction Control** dialogue box with direction set to **Clockwise**

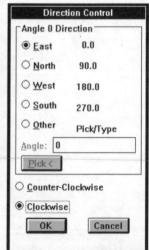

Note

When any form of circular motion is required, the default counter clockwise (anti-clockwise) motion can be changed to a clockwise motion in the **Direction Control** dialogue box called from **Units Style...** in the **Settings** pull-down menu as shown in Fig. 4.12.

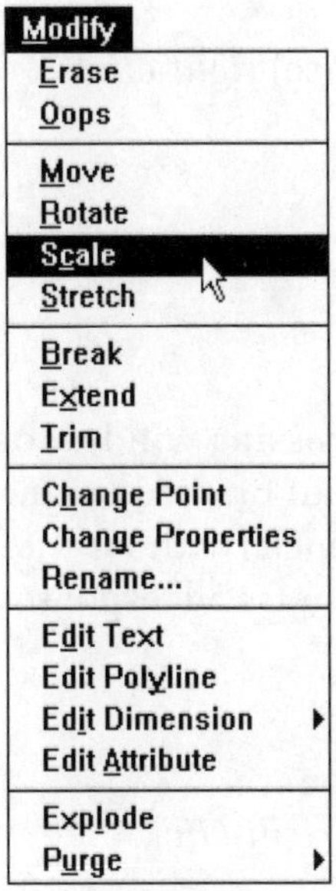

The tool SCALE

If the drawing, or part of a drawing to be scaled, consists of several entities, a window will be required to surround the entities – or a crossing window could be used to cross the entities. Drawings 2 and 3 of Fig. 4.14 show examples:

Command: SCALE
Select objects: *enter* w (for Window) *right-click*
First corner: *pick* **Other corner:** *pick* **3 found**
Select objects: *right-click*
Base point: *pick*
<Scale factor>/Reference: *enter* the scale factor figure *right-click*
Command:

If a single entity is to be scaled – e.g. the pline outline (Drawing 1 of Fig. 4.14):

Command: SCALE
Select objects: *left-click* on the entity
Select objects: *right-click*
Base point: *pick*
<Scale factor>/Reference: *enter* the scale factor figure *right-click*
Command:

Fig. 4.13 Calling **Scale**

Fig. 4.14 Examples of scaling using the **Scale** tool

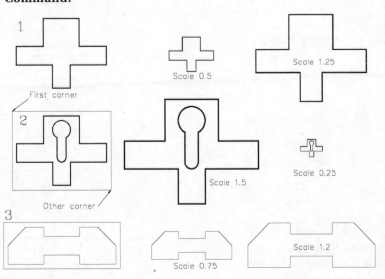

Another method of entering the scale is to use the prompt **Reference** as follows:

Command: SCALE
Select objects: *enter* w (for Window) *right-click*
First corner: *pick* **Other corner:** *pick* **3 found**
Select objects: *right-click*
Base point: *pick*
<Scale factor>/Reference: *enter* r (for Reference) *right-click*
Reference length <1>: *right-click*
New length: *enter* the scale figure *right-click*
Command:

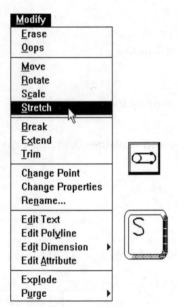

Fig. 4.15 Calling **Stretch**

The tool STRETCH

This tool is always used in conjunction with a **crossing** window or with a **fence**. If one attempts to use the tool without first requesting a crossing window (with w for Window) or a fence (with an f for polygon Fence), the tool will not function. The prompts and responses are always the same:

Command: STRETCH
Select objects to stretch by window or polygon...
Select objects: *enter* c (for crossing Window) *right-click*
First corner: *pick* **Other corner:** *pick* **1 found**
Select objects: *right-click*
Base point of displacement: *pick*
Second point of displacement: *pick*
Command:

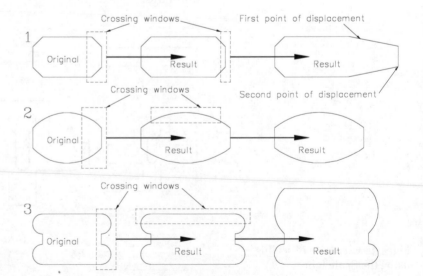

Fig. 4.16 Examples of the results of using the **Stretch** tool

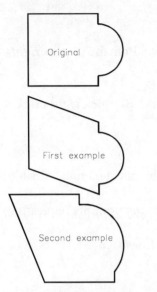

Fig. 4.17 Further examples of the results of using the **Stretch** tool

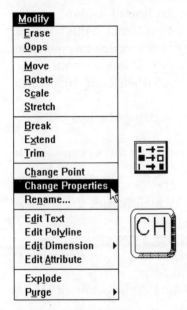

Fig. 4.18 Calling **Change**

Notes

1. A **fence** is similar in action to a crossing window except that a fence is made up from a number of lines to form a polygon rather than a crossing window in the form of a rectangle. In all cases where a crossing window can be used in AutoCAD LT, the response **f** will enable a polygon fence to be used in place of a crossing window. The advantage of a fence is that it can take the form of a polygon with as many sides as the operator wishes and can be drawn to take in features which would not be possible with the rectangular crossing window. All entities crossed by the polygonal fence are selected.

2. **Stretch** can have an unexpected result when used across arcs or circles. This is shown in Fig. 4.16 which shows the effects of stretching across arcs.

3. Fig. 4.17 shows the effect of the points of displacement not being taken vertically or horizontally.

The tool CHANGE

Two types of change can carried out with the aid of this tool – Fig. 4.19. Other types of change will be understood when the **ELEV** command is explained – see **Notes** overleaf.

First example – changing linetype

Command: CHANGE
Select objects: *pick* the line
Select objects: *right-click*
Property/<Change point>: *enter* p (for Property) *right-click*
Change what property (Color/Elev/LAyer/LType/Thickness)? *enter* lt (for LType) *right-click*
New linetype <by LAYER>: *enter* centre *right-click*
Command:

Second example – changing text style

Command: CHANGE
Select objects: *left-click* on the text

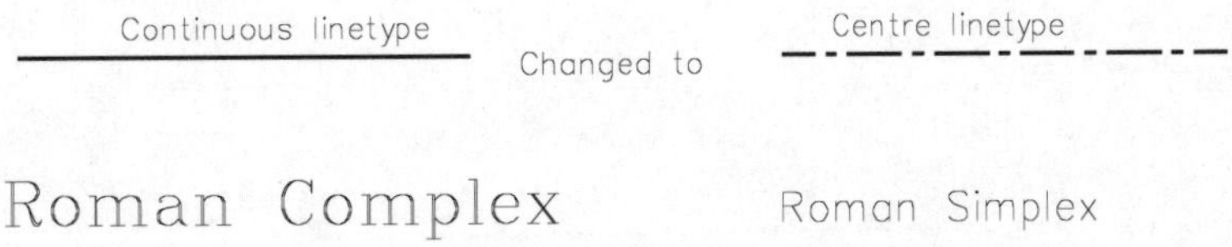

Fig. 4.19 Two examples of the results of using the **Change** tool

Continuous linetype ———————— Changed to —·—·—·—·— Centre linetype

Roman Complex   Roman Simplex

Select objects: *right-click*
Property/<Change point>: *pick* a point
New style or RETURN for no change: *enter* Roman Simplex *right-click*
New rotation angle <0>:
New text (Roman Complex): *enter* Roman Simplex *right-click*
Command:

Notes

1. When changing text style, the style for the new text must already have been loaded – see p. 48.
2. The reader should attempt changes using the prompts requesting **Color** and **Layer**.
3. The meanings of **Elev**ation and **Thickness** are described in Chapter 13.

Questions

1. What is the purpose of the **Undo** command?
2. If you make a mistake when using the **Erase** tool, how can the mistake be rectified? Note – this is not explained in this book, but the reader should find no difficulty in answering this question. Look at the tools shown in the **Modify** pull-down menu.
3. In which direction is a break performed when using **Break** on an arc?
4. How can the direction of rotation be changed when using the **Rotate** tool?
5. If you wish to extend a line by 50 units and there is no entity to extend to, what action can you take?
6. What is the purpose of the **Trim** tool?
7. Can you scale an individual entity which is part of a group of entities without scaling the whole group?
8. What happens if you attempt stretching a circle?
9. If you wish to change the text style of text in your drawing to another style, what must you first do?
10. What is meant by a **fence** in relation to the selection of objects when using a tool?

Exercises

1. Draw a series of lines vertically and horizontally with the **Dline** tool set to a width of 15 as shown in the left hand drawing of Fig. 4.20. Then with the aid of **Trim** produce the right hand drawing of Fig. 4.20.

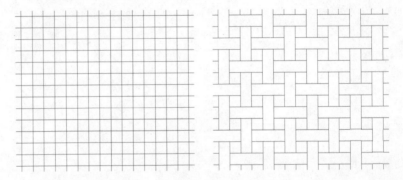

Fig. 4.20 Exercise 1

2. Fig. 4.21 shows the hour hand of a clock set at 12:00. Copy the given drawing, then with the aid of the tool **Copy** make 5 further copies. In the 5 copies **Rotate** the hour hand to the hours of 2:00. 4:00, 6:00, 8:00 and 10:00 respectively. Do not attempt adding dimensions.

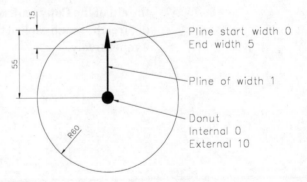

Fig. 4.21 Exercise 2

3.   Copy Fig. 4.22 to the dimensions given. With the aid of the **Copy** tool copy your drawing 3 times. With the **Scale** tool scale the first two drawings to 1.5 times and 0.4 times scale respectively. Within your third copy scale each of the circles to a scale of 0.75. Do not attempt including the dimensions.

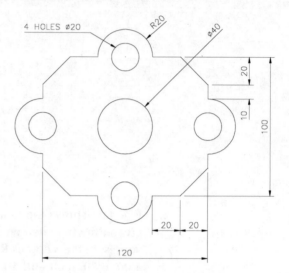

Fig. 4.22 Exercise 3

4.   Copy Drawing 1 of Fig. 4.23 to the given dimensions. Then with the aid of the **Copy** tool, copy your drawing 3 times. With the aid of **Stretch** stretch each of the copies as shown in drawings 2, 3 and 4 repetitively.

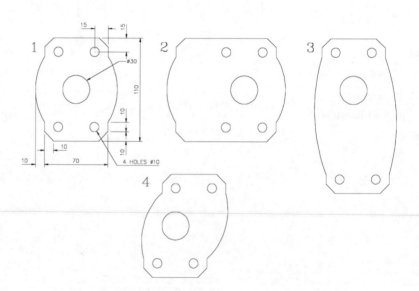

Fig. 4.23 Exercise 4

5. Copy the pline and the text in Fig. 4.24. With the aid of the **Change** tool change the pline first to a centre line, then to a hidden line. Then change the text to **Italic Complex** text 15 high.

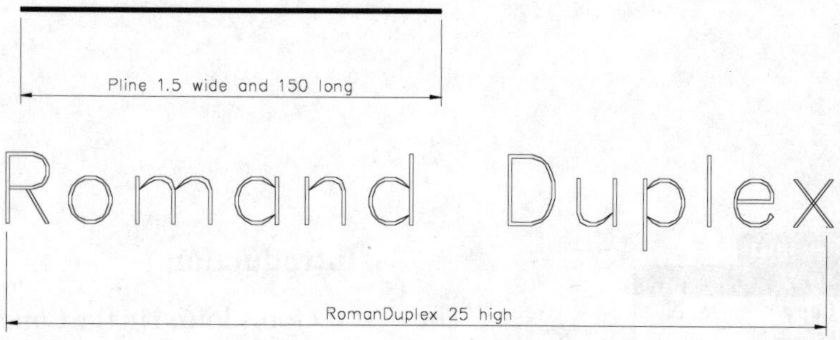

Pline 1.5 wide and 150 long

Romand Duplex

RomanDuplex 25 high

Fig. 4.24 Exercise 5

CHAPTER 5

The Construct commands

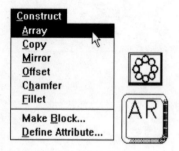

Fig. 5.1 Calling **Array**

Introduction

The first six tools found in the **Construct** pull-down menu are among those which allow drawings to be speedily constructed in CAD operations. For this reason they will be dealt with in some depth in this chapter. The last two commands in **Construct** will be dealt with in later chapters.

The tool ARRAY

The first example – of a **Polar** array – is given in Fig. 5.2.

> **Command: ARRAY**
> **Select objects:** *pick* objects
> **Rectangular or Polar array (R/P) <P>:** *right-click* (accept P)
> **Center point of array:** *pick* or *enter* coordinates
> **Number of items:** *enter* 12 (required number) *right-click*
> **Angle to fill (+=ccw, −=cw) <360>:** *right-click* (accept 360)
> **Rotate objects as they are copied? <Y>:** *right-click*
> (accept Y)
> **Command:**

The second example of a **Polar** array – Fig. 5.3 – shows one in which the **Angle to fill** has been *entered* as 180°. Note the minus sign in

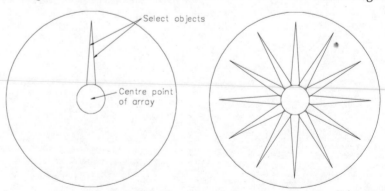

Fig. 5.2 Two stages of the first example – Polar array of 360°

front of the **Angle to fill** number, allowing a clockwise (cw) array. Note also that the 180° angle lies through the centre line of the selected object – one only in this example because it is a pline.

Command: ARRAY
Select objects: *pick* objects
Rectangular or Polar array (R/P) <P>: *right-click* (accept P)
Center point of array: *pick* or *enter* coordinates
Number of items: *enter* 6 (required number) *right-click*
Angle to fill (+=ccw, –=cw) <360>: *enter* -180 *right-click*
Rotate objects as they are copied? <Y>: *right-click* (accept Y)
Command:

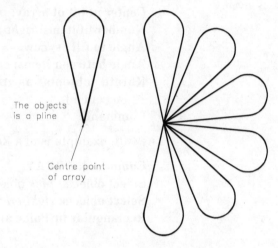

The objects is a pline

Centre point of array

Fig. 5.3 Second example – a **Polar** array of 180°

The third example – Fig. 5.4 – shows a **Polar** array in which the response to the prompt **Rotate objects as they are copied?** is n (No).

Command: ARRAY
Select objects: *pick* objects
Rectangular or Polar array (R/P) <P>: *right-click* (accept P)
Center point of array: *pick* or *enter* coordinates

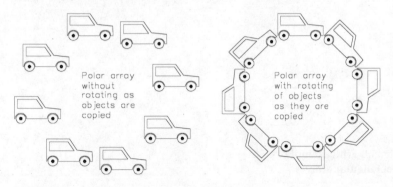

Polar array without rotating as objects are copied

Polar array with rotating of objects as they are copied

Fig. 5.4 Third example of a **Polar** array in which objects have not been rotated in the array

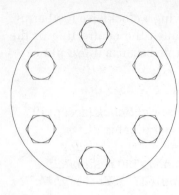

Fig. 5.5 Fourth example of a **Polar** array in which the angle between items is given

Number of items: *enter* 8 (required number) *right-click*
Angle to fill (+=ccw, −=cw) <360>: *right-click*
Rotate objects as they are copied? <Y>: *enter* n *right-click*
Command:

In Fig. 5.4 the right hand drawing compares the array with rotation of the objects with the left-hand drawing in which rotation of the objects does not occur.

The fourth example – Fig. 5.5 – if, at the **Number of items** prompt, a *right-click* is given, the angle between the items will be requested:

Command: ARRAY
Select objects: *pick* objects
Rectangular or Polar array (R/P) <P>: *right-click* (accept P)
Center point of array: *pick* or *enter* coordinates
Number of items: *right-click*
Angle to fill (+=ccw, −=cw) <360>: *right-click*
Angle between items: *enter* 60 *right-click*
Rotate objects as they are copied? <Y>: *right-click* (accept Y)
Command:

The fifth example is of a **Rectangular** array:

Command: ARRAY
Select objects: *pick* objects **6 found**
Select objects: *right-click*
Rectangular or Polar array (R/P) <P>: *enter* r (Rectangular)

Original
drawing

Fig. 5.6 Fifth example - a **Rectangular** array

right-click
Number of rows(---)<1>: *enter* 5 *right-click*
Number of columns (I I I):<1>: *enter* 4 *right-click*
Unit cell or distance between rows (---): *enter* −70 *right-click*
Distance between columns (I I I): *enter* 60 *right-click*
Command:

Notes

1. It will be seen in the above sequence that the distance between rows was entered as a minus number. This is because:
   +ve *x* coordinates are to the right
   −ve *x* coordinates are to the left
   +ve y coordinates are upwards
   −ve y coordinates are downwards
2. The unit distance of items between rows or columns is taken from the same point in each of the parts of the items in the array. For example you can take the distance from the centre of your item or from the bottom left corner – or, in fact, at any point on the item.

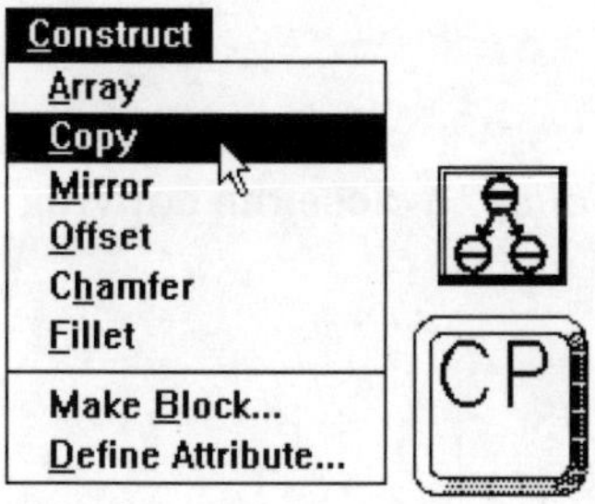

Fig. 5.7 Calling **Copy**

The tool COPY

There are two main methods of using the **Copy** tool – the default option – to copy an item once only – or to copy an item many times over – the **Multiple** option. Fig. 5.8 shows both options in the same illustration. Drawing 1 shows the single copy option, Drawing 2 the multiple copy option.

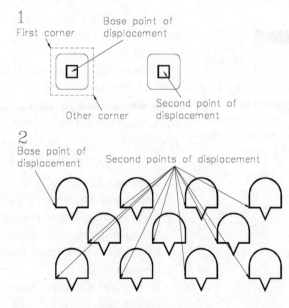

Fig. 5.8 Examples of the results of using the **Copy** tool

The command for the default option will show the following sequence:

Command: COPY
Select objects: *enter* w (Window) *right-click*
First corner: *pick* **Other corner:** *pick* **2 found**
Select objects: *right-click*
<Base point of displacement>Multiple: *pick* a suitable point
Second point of displacement: *pick* a suitable point
Command:

The command line sequence for the multiple copy option will be:

Command: COPY
Select objects: *left-click* on the item to be copied
Select objects: *right-click*
<Base point of displacement>Multiple: *enter* m (Multiple) *right-click*
Base point: *pick*
Second point of displacement: *pick*
Second point of displacement: *pick*
Second point of displacement: *pick*
Second point of displacement: *pick*
Second point of displacement: *pick*
Second point of displacement: *right-click* to close the copying
Command:

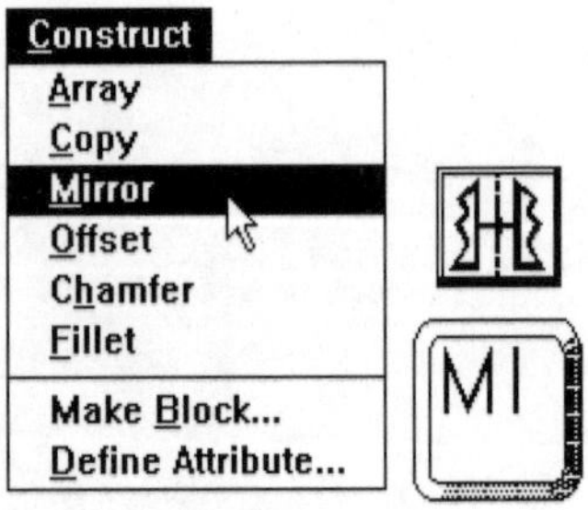

The tool MIRROR

This tool allows the copying of a mirror image of a drawing or part of a drawing. Either the original drawing can be retained or it can be deleted during the series of options which appear with the tool. Drawings 1 and 2 in Fig. 5.10 give examples of the use of the tool when both the originals and the mirror images are retained.

If one wishes to **Mirror** text, either on its own, or as part of a drawing, care must be taken to set the variable **Mirrtext**. The two possible settings (0 or 1) and the results of the settings are shown in Drawings 3 and 4 of Fig. 5.10.

Command: MIRROR
Select objects: *enter* w (Window) *right-click*
First corner: Other corner: 3 found
Select objects: *right-click*
First point on mirror line:
Second point:
Delete old objects?<N>:
Command:

Construct
Array
Copy
Mirror
Offset
Chamfer
Fillet

Make **B**lock...
Define Attribute...

Fig. 5.9 Calling **Mirror**

Fig. 5.10 Examples of the
results of using the tool
Mirror

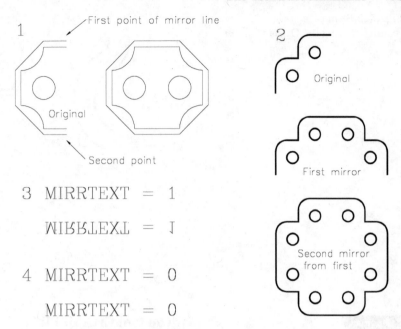

3   MIRRTEXT = 1

MIRRTEXT = 1

4   MIRRTEXT = 0

MIRRTEXT = 0

To set the **Mirrtext** variable *enter* mirrtext at the command prompt,
followed by a *right-click* and respond to the prompt which appears:

> **Command:** *enter* mirrtext *right-click*
> **New value for MIRRTEXT<0>:** *enter* 1 *right-click*
> **Command:**

and the variable is set to mirror text either upside down vertically or
backwards horizontally.

The tool OFFSET

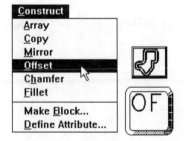

Fig. 5.11 Calling **Offset**

The distance through which an item is to be offset can either be
entered as a figure (representing numbers of units) or by the selection
by *picking* of two points the required distance apart on the screen.
If several offsets are required through the same distance one after the
other, the **Select side to offset:** prompt is repeated until a *right-click*
terminates the offsetting. Several examples are given in Fig. 5.12.

The command line sequence always follows the pattern:

> **Command: OFFSET**
> **Offset distance or Through<Through>:** *enter* a figure *right-click*
> **Select object to offset:** *pick* the object or window an item
> **Select side to offset:** *pick* the required side
> **Select side to offset:** *right-click* to finish offsetting
> **Command:**

Fig. 5.12 Examples of the
results of using the **Offset** tool

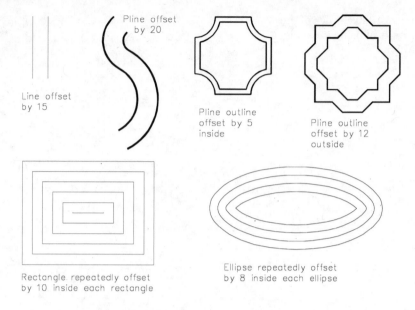

The tool CHAMFER

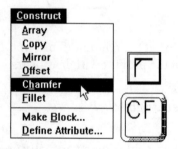

Fig. 5.13 Calling **Chamfer**

The tool CHAMFER

Five examples of the results of using the **Chamfer** tool are illustrated
in Fig. 5.14. These are:

1. Using the tool on two lines meeting at a corner. A clean chamfer is
   formed.
2. Chamfering all corners of a pline rectangle. All corners can be
   chamfered with one selection.
3. Chamfering a single corner of a pline rectangle. If required a single
   corner of a pline can be chamfered.
4. Chamfering lines not meeting at a corner. The lines are joined into
   the chamfer.
5. Chamfering lines crossing at a corner. The lines are joined by the
   chamfer.

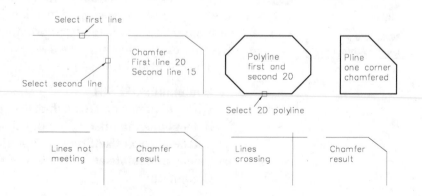

Fig. 5.14 Examples of the
results of using the tool
Chamfer

When the tool is called, it is first necessary to set the distances along the edges to be chamfered, unless they are already known and suitable:

> **Command: CHAMFER**
> **Polyline/Distances/<Select first line>:** *enter* d (Distance) *right-click*
> **Enter first chamfer distance<10>:** *enter* figures *right-click*
> **Enter second chamfer distance<10>:** *enter* figures *right-click*
> **Command:**
> **Polyline/Distances/<Select first line>:** *pick* first line
> **Select second line:** *pick* second line
> **Chamfer:**

If a closed pline is to be chamfered at all corners:

> **Polyline/Distances/<Select first line>:** *enter* p (Polyline) *right-click*
> **Select 2D polyline:** *pick* anywhere on the pline
> **Command:**

As can be seen in Fig. 5.14, if only one corner of a closed pline is to be chamfered, the two lines bounding the chamfer will be picked as first and second lines.

If two separate plines meet at a corner they cannot be chamfered with the tool. If an attempt is made the following warning appears:

> **Cannot chamfer segments of different polylines**

The tool FILLET

This tool works in much the same manner as does the **Chamfer** tool, except that only one distance – the radius of the fillet – has to be set. Examples are given in Fig. 5.16.

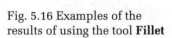

Fig. 5.15 Calling **Fillet**

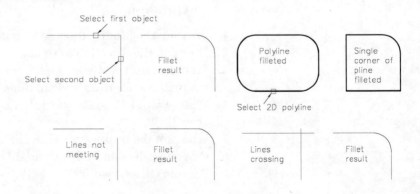

Fig. 5.16 Examples of the results of using the tool **Fillet**

Command: FILLET
Polyline/Radius/<Select first object>: *enter* r (Radius) *right-click*
Enter fillet radius<0>: *enter* radius figures *right-click*
Command:
Polyline/Radius/<Select first object>: *pick* object
Select second object: *pick* object
Command:

Notes

1. Fig. 5.17. If **Chamfer** distances are both set to 0, or the **Fillet** radius is set to 0, when the tools are used on lines which do not meet at corners, the lines make a perfect join. The same applies to lines crossing each other at corners. This facility is sometimes of value if a construction has been drawn with lines which should join at corners and do not meet exactly.
2. Also shown in Fig. 5.17. Lines will fillet exactly to circles, but the ends of crossing arcs or lines crossing arcs will fillet as shown.

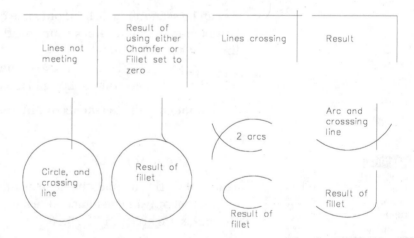

Fig. 5.17 Closing corners with either **Chamfer** or **Fillet** and using **Fillet** on arcs, lines and circles

Questions

1. Why are the **Modify** tools so important?
2. How can the direction of rotation of a Polar array be changed?
3. From where on an item which is being Rectangularly arrayed will the distance for rows and columns be taken?
4. When would you use Multiple Copy in place of a Rectangular array?
5. What are the settings of MIRRTEXT?
6. Do you understand what a variable is in AutoCAD LT?
7. What is **Offset** used for?

8. What is the difference between chamfering a closed pline and chamfering two separate plines meeting at an angle?
9. When would it be of value to set either **Chamfer** distances or a **Fillet** radius to zero?
10. If two crossing arcs are acted upon with the **Fillet** tool what would you expect the result to be?

Exercises

1. Fig. 5.18 shows an engineering component which has been drawn with the aid of the **Array** tool. Fig. 5.19 is a three-dimensional view of the component. Using your discretion about dimensions, make a copy of Fig. 5.18.

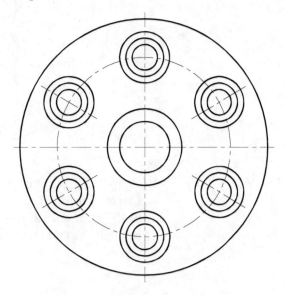

Fig. 5.18 Exercise 1

Fig. 5.19 Exercise 1. A 3D rendering of the component

2. Fig. 5.20. Make an accurate copy of the drawing working to the dimensions included with the drawing. Fig. 5.20 is constructed from plines, but if you wish you could use lines and circles instead of plines.

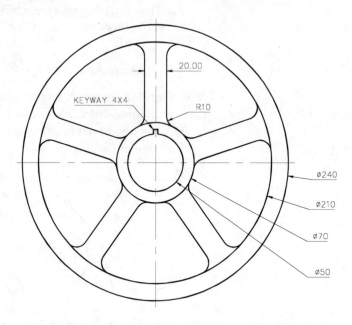

Fig. 5.20 Exercise 2

3. Fig. 5.21. Using your own discretion about sizes and working with **Circle**, **Arc** and **Trim** tools copy the larger drawing of the outline of the rear of a sitting cat. Then **Scale** your drawing to 0.4 of its original size and using the **Array** tool construct the given rectangular array.

Fig. 5.21 Exercise 3

4. Fig. 5.22. Copy the outline labelled **Original** using the **Pline** tool set to a width of 1. Then with **Mirror** complete the outline for the rectangular array. Then construct the rectangular array using the **Array** tool. Use your own discretion about sizes.

Fig. 5.22 Exercise 4

5. Fig. 5.23. The left-hand drawing shows sizes and shapes of the parts of the compass. Use: **Arc, Mirror, Pline, Circle, Donut** and **Array**.

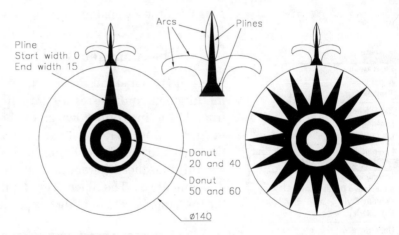

Fig. 5.23 Exercise 5

6. Fig. 5.24. Details given with the drawing. Construct the right-hand drawing.

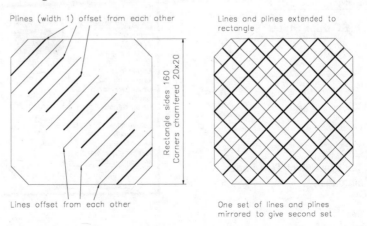

Fig. 5.24 Exercise 6

CHAPTER 6

Text

Introduction

We have already used text to a limited extent. Text in drawings constructed in AutoCAD LT is of sufficient importance to warrant a fuller description. The font for text is set by the command **Style**. Two forms of text fonts are available in AutoCAD LT – Postscript fonts held in files with an extension of *.fpb* and AutoCAD fonts held in files with the extension *.shx*.

The command STYLE

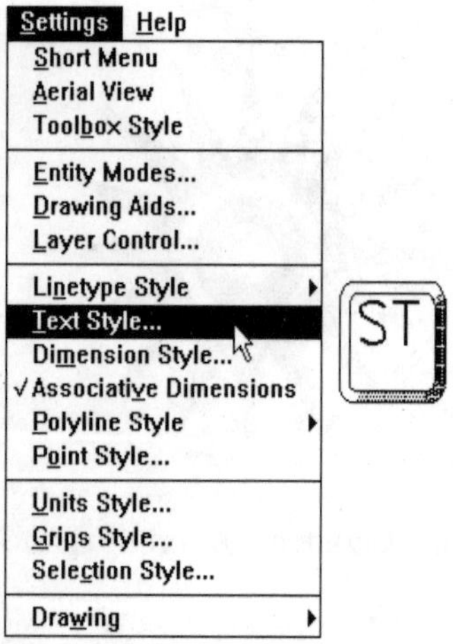

There are two methods by which **Styles** can be called (Fig. 6.1), but for this command, the results are different. If **Text Style...** is selected from the **Settings** pull-down menu the **Select Text Font** dialogue box – Fig. 6.2 appears. If **st** or **styles** is entered at the command line from the keyboard, the **Select Font File** dialogue box appears. The reader should note the differences in the names of the fonts in the two dialogue boxes. The **Select Text Font** box shows the full names for the font, the Select **Font File** box shows the font filename. No matter

Fig. 6.1 Calling **Styles**

Fig. 6.2 The **Select Text Font** dialogue box

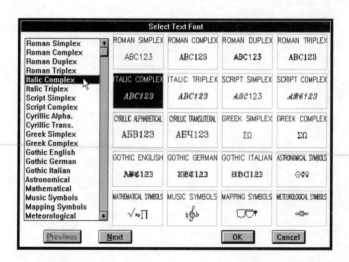

Fig. 6.3 The **Select Font File**
dialogue box

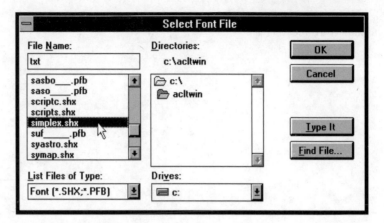

which of the two methods is used for calling the command, the
command line will show a similar series of prompts for setting the
parameters for the text style. The following show the prompts when
st is entered at the command line, but the prompts for selecting from
the **Select Text Font** dialogue box require the same parameter
settings:

> **Command: STYLE**
> **Text style name (or ?)<STANDARD>:** *enter* simplex *right-click*
> **New style. Height<0>:** *enter* the required height figure *right-click*
> **Width factor<1>:** *right-click* (accept)
> **Obliquing angle <0>:** *right-click* (accept)
> **Backwards?<N>:** *right-click* (accept)
> **Upside down?<N>:** *right-click* (accept)
> **Vertical?<N>:** *right-click* (accept)
> **SIMPLEX is now the current text style**
> **Command:**

Fig. 6.4 shows the main text font styles available in AutoCAD LT. In
addition there are fonts for astronomical, musical, mathematical,
mapping and meteorological symbols as well as many others. If the
reader scrolls the list box in the **Select Text Font** dialogue box, the
complete list of available fonts will be seen. All the text or symbols
in a font file can be seen if required. *Left-click* on **Entity Modes...** in
the **Settings** pull-down menu, followed by a *left-click* on the **Text
Style...** button in the resulting dialogue box, followed by a *left-click*
on the **Show All...** button in the **Select Text Style** box which appears.
As shown in Fig. 6.5 in which the mathematical symbols are the
current style all the symbols are shown in the resulting **Text Style
Symbol Set** box.

Postscript fonts
cbt___.fpb 8 high
cobt___.pfb 10 high
eur___pfb 8 high
euro___.pfb 10 high
par_.pfb 10 high
rom___.pfb 10 high
romb___.pfb 8 high
romi___.pfb 10 high
sas___.pfb 12 high
sasb___.pfb 12 high
sasbo___.pfb 12 high
saso___.pfb 12 high
SUF___.PFB 12 HIGH
TE___.PFB 12 HIGH
AutoCAD fonts
complex.shx 8 high
iso9.sxh 8 high
italic.shx 10 high
monotxt.shx 10 high
romand.shx 8 high
romant.shx 10 high
simplex.shx 8 high
scriptc.shx 12 high
scripts.shx 12 high
gothice.shx 12 high
gothicg.shx 12 high
gothici.shx 12 high

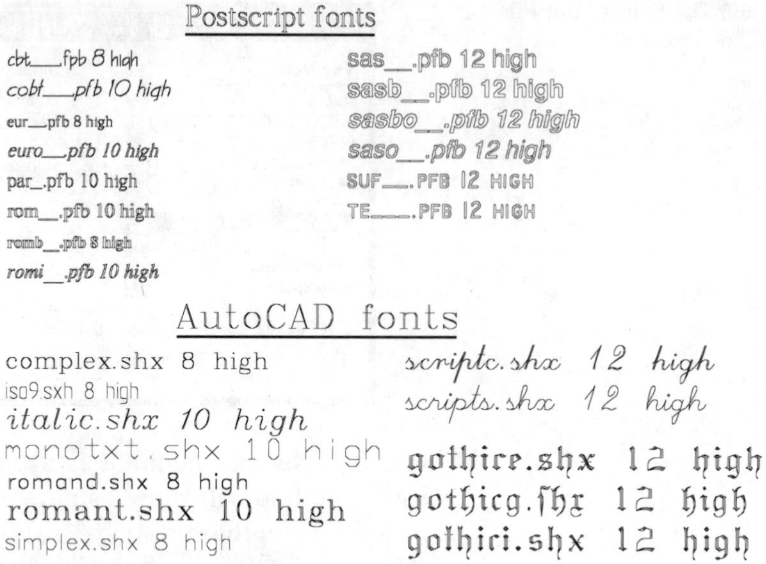

Fig. 6.4 The font styles available in AutoCAD LT

Entity Creation Modes
Color...
BYLAYER
Layer...
0
Linetype...
BYLAYER
Text Style...
SYMATH
Elevation:
0
Thickness:
0
OK
Cancel
Select Text Style
S
STANDARD
SYMATH
Text Style SYMATH Symbol Set
%&' ()*+,−./0123456789:;<=>?@

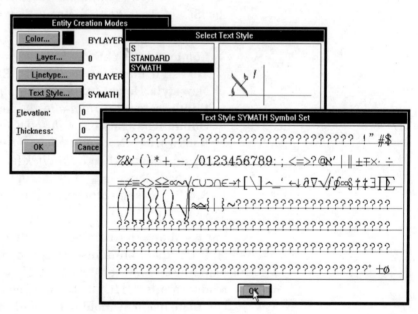

Fig. 6.5 The **Text Style Symbol Set** box

The tool TEXT

When text is called, the command line shows:

Command: *enter* t *right-click*
DTEXT Justify/Style/<Start point>:

If the response is to *enter* s (for Style) the command line changes:

DTEXT Justify/Style/<Start point>: *enter* s *right-click*
Style name (or ?)<STANDARD>:

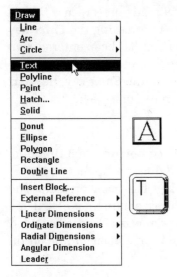

Fig. 6.6 Calling **Text**

Only the text styles already loaded in the current drawing are available from this **Style** prompt in the **Text** prompts series. If uncertain as to which text styles have been loaded, *enter* ? followed by two *right-clicks* and a text screen appears listing the currently loaded text files.

If the response is to *enter* j (for Justify) the command line changes:

DTEXT Justify/Style/<Start point>: *enter* j *right-click*
Align/Fit/Center/Middle/Right:

Fig. 6.7 shows the results of responses to these justification prompts, in addition to showing text which has been rotated through 90°. Note that when aligning text, its height will not be the expected height as set with the **Style** command, but will accommodate to the alignment.

If the default **<Start point>:** response is accepted by either *entering* coordinates or by *picking* a point on screen, the command line changes:

DTEXT Justify/Style/<Start point>: *pick*
Rotation angle <0>: *right-click* (to accept the angle of 0°)
Text: *enter* the required text

As the text is entered, because it is dynamic text (Dtext), a square appears on screen enclosing each letter or figure as it is *entered* at the keyboard. When a line of text has been entered, followed by pressing the *Enter* key of the keyboard (**NOT** a *right-click*) a second line of text

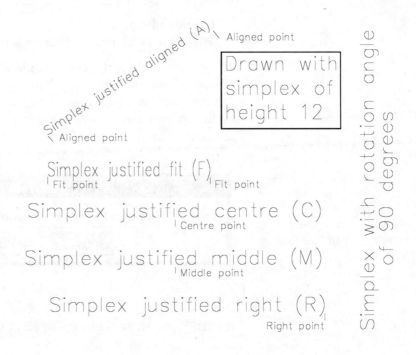

Fig. 6.7 Examples of positioning of text

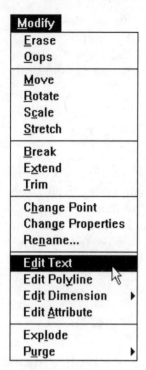

Fig. 6.8 Selecting **Edit Text** from the **Modify** pull-down menu

can be entered immediately below that already on screen. Lines of text can be entered one below the other by pressing the *Enter* key after each line of text. When all required text has been entered, two presses of the *Enter* key brings the text to an end. It should however be noted that after any one of the presses of the *Enter* key, the start point can be changed by *picking* a new point on screen.

Non-dynamic text

If the word **text** is *entered* in full, the text command is not **Dtext**. As the text is entered at the command line, it does not appear on screen until either a *right-click* or the *Enter* key has been pressed. The command line then changes to **Command:** To obtain lines of text one after the other, a *right-click* will now allow a second line to be added and so on until the desired lines of text have been produced on screen.

Note

The abbreviation for text is **TX**. This means that when tx is *entered* at the command line in place of the full word **text**, the text will not be entered on the screen dynamically as it is when t is *entered*.

Editing text

Left-click on **Edit Text** in the **Modify** pull-down menu – Fig. 6.8. The command line changes to:

Command:
<Select a TEXT or ATTDEF object>/Undo:

Left-click on the text which requires to be edited. The **Edit Text** dialogue box appears – Fig. 6.9. The text object appears in the window and can be changed as required in the window. A *left-click* on the **OK** button of the dialogue box and the text which was selected is changed to the edited text.

Fig. 6.9 The **Edit Text** dialogue box

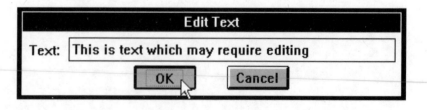

Note

ATTDEF objects will be explained in Chapter 7.

Questions

1. How many types of fonts are available in AutoCAD LT?
2. What is the purpose of the command **Style**?
3. What is the file extension given to the files holding AutoCAD text styles?
4. What is the file extension given to the other type of fonts available in AutoCAD?
5. How can you check on the font style as being that which you wish to use?
6. What are the justifications available when text is called?
7. What difference would you expect if, instead of calling the text command by *entering* a t at the keyboard, you *entered* text in full?

Exercises

1. Fig. 6.10. Either make an accurate copy of the given order form or design one of your own. Use text styles and sizes which you believe to be suitable.

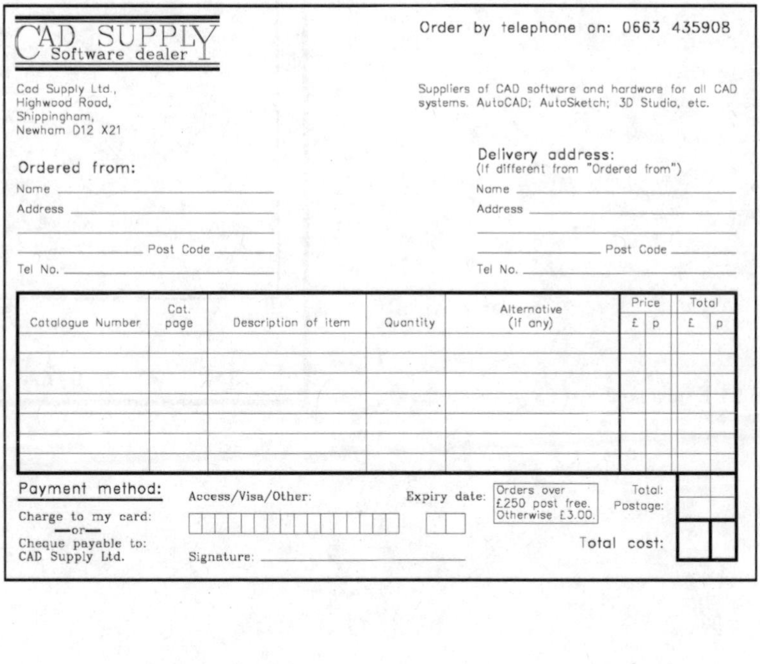

CAD SUPPLY
Software dealer

Order by telephone on: 0663 435908

Cad Supply Ltd.,
Highwood Road,
Shippingham,
Newham D12 X21

Suppliers of CAD software and hardware for all CAD systems. AutoCAD; AutoSketch; 3D Studio, etc.

Ordered from:
Name
Address
Post Code
Tel No.

Delivery address:
(If different from "Ordered from")
Name
Address
Post Code
Tel No.

Catalogue Number	Cat. page	Description of item	Quantity	Alternative (if any)	Price £	Price p	Total £	Total p

Payment method:
Charge to my card:
—or—
Cheque payable to:
CAD Supply Ltd.
Access/Visa/Other:
Expiry date:
Signature:
Orders over £250 post free. Otherwise £3.00.
Total:
Postage:
Total cost:

Fig. 6.10 Exercise 1

2. Fig. 6.11. Either copy the given map complete with its text, or design a similar map of your own choice based on a suitable destination within the area in which you live. Use **DLINE** for the roads and **TRIM** to fit the roads in and around roundabouts.

3. Fig. 6.12. This exercise attempts to show how you could design your own text style for a particular purpose. Use your own discretion about sizes of the grid and the circles. The given drawing shows three stages in the designing of the name **AutoCAD LT**.

4. Fig. 3.8 on page 49 shows a prototype drawing which includes borders and a title block. Working to the pattern of drawing layout suggested by Fig. 3.8 construct your own prototype drawing file.

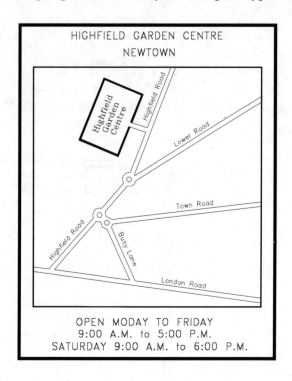

Fig. 6.11 Exercise 2

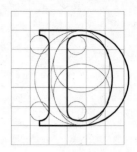

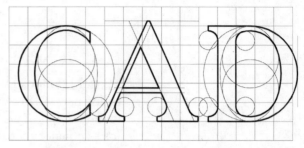

Fig. 6.12 Exercise 3

CHAPTER 7

Wblocks, blocks and inserts

Introduction

The tool **Wblock** allows the insertion of any AutoCAD LT drawing, or any part of a drawing into another AutoCAD LT drawing. This tool (command) is of particular importance when constructing drawings for two major reasons:

1. By using existing drawings or parts of existing drawings, it is possible to add drawings from files already saved on disk rather than having to construct new drawings of features, thus speeding up the drawing process considerably.
2. The use of wblocks allows the drawing of circuit diagrams of all types to be readily and quickly constructed without the need to repeatedly construct symbols.

The reader should be aware of the difference between a wblock and a block. Whereas a wblock (or written block) is a drawing file which can be inserted into any other drawing, a block can only exist in the drawing into which it was inserted. If a wblock is inserted into a drawing, it becomes a block in that drawing and can be used several times within the drawing.

There are a number of dialogue boxes associated with blocks and the insertion of blocks within drawings.

The tool WBLOCK

When a wblock is created it is saved as an AutoCAD drawing file with the filename extension *.dwg* in the selected directory, in the same way as for any other AutoCAD drawing file. To operate the tool (command), *enter* w (for wblock) from the keyboard and the command line changes:

Command: *enter* w (for Wblock) *right-click* **Create Drawing File**
dialogue box appears. *Enter* a filename in the dialogue box
WBLOCK

Block name: *right-click* (accepts the entered filename)
Insertion base point: *pick* or *enter* coordinates
Select objects: *enter* w (for Window)
First corner: *pick* or *enter* coordinates
Other corner: *pick* or *enter* coordinates **21 found**
Command:

Fig. 7.1 shows the sequence of events which occur in response to the creation of a wblock with the filename *bolt01.dwg*. Fig. 7.2 shows the **Create Drawing File** dialogue box which appears directly the command is called.

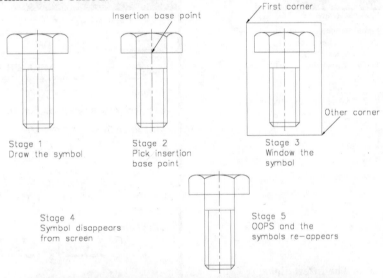

Fig. 7.1 The stages in creating a **Wblock**

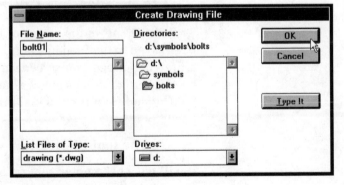

Fig. 7.2 The **Create Drawing File** dialogue box in which the wblock drawing filename is entered

The tool INSERT

Any AutoCAD drawing, whether saved as a Wblock or otherwise, can be inserted into any other AutoCAD drawing with the aid of this tool called either from the **Draw** pull-down menu or by *entering* i (for insert) at the command line. The abbreviation i represents **Ddinsert** , which calls up the dialogue box **Insert:**

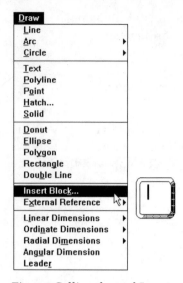

Fig. 7.3 Calling the tool **Insert**

Command: *enter* i (for ddinsert) *right-click* the **Insert** dialogue box appears (Fig. 7.4)

DDINSERT Insertion point: the block appears with the intersection of the cursor hairs as its insertion point (Fig. 7.5). *Pick* a point for the insertion of the block

X scale factor <1>/Corner/XYZ: *right-click* (to accept)

Y scale factor (default=X): *right-click* (to accept)

Rotation angle: *right-click* (to accept)

Command:

Fig. 7.4 The **Insert** dialogue box

```
┌──────────────────────── Insert ────────────────────────┐
│ ┌─Select Block Name─────────────────────────────────┐  │
│ │  ┌────────┐   ┌──────────────────────────────┐    │  │
│ │  │ Block... │   │ BOLT01                       │    │  │
│ │  └────────┘   └──────────────────────────────┘    │  │
│ │  ┌────────┐   ┌──────────────────────────────┐    │  │
│ │  │ File...  │   │ D:\SYMBOLS\BOLTS\BOLT01.DWG   │    │  │
│ │  └────────┘   └──────────────────────────────┘    │  │
│ └───────────────────────────────────────────────────┘  │
│ ┌─Options───────────────────────────────────────────┐  │
│ │  ⊠ Specify Parameters on Screen                    │  │
│ │  ┌Insertion Point┐ ┌Scale─┐    ┌Rotation──────┐   │  │
│ │  X: [0]           X: [1]        Angle: [0]        │  │
│ │  Y: [0]           Y: [1]                          │  │
│ │  Z: [0]           Z: [1]                          │  │
│ └───────────────────────────────────────────────────┘  │
│ □ Explode                                               │
│       ┌──────┐    ┌────────┐    ┌───────┐               │
│       │  OK  │    │ Cancel │    │ Help...│              │
│       └──────┘    └────────┘    └───────┘               │
└─────────────────────────────────────────────────────────┘
```

Fig. 7.5 shows the stages of insertion of the wblock which has been saved to the filename *bolt01.dwg* inserted into position within a drawing already on screen. In this example, once the block had been inserted, details of a washer had to be added and parts had to be trimmed from the original drawing.

The tool EXPLODE

It will have been noted that, in Stage 4 of Fig. 7.5, the bolt drawing was exploded into its entities in order that some editing was possible. Note also in the **Insert** dialogue box (Fig. 7.4) a box labelled **Explode** had not been checked. Unless the **Explode** box has been checked in the dialogue box a wblock is inserted in position on screen as a single entity, allowing it to be moved, copied, mirrored, scaled and/or stretched as a single entity. If parts of an unexploded wblock require editing/modifying, it must first be exploded:

Fig. 7.5 Stages in inserting the wblock **bolt01.dwg**

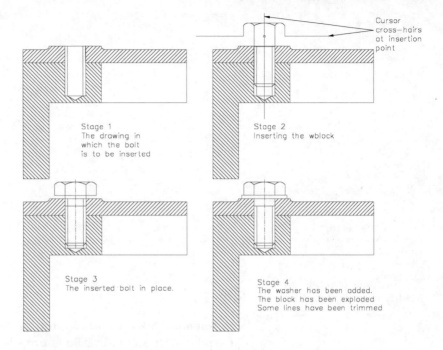

Command: *enter* x (for explode) *right-click*
EXPLODE
Select objects: *left-click* on the block to be exploded **1 found**
Select objects: *right-click*
Command:

and the wblock is exploded into its constituent entities.

Modifying a wblock

Fig. 7.6 shows some examples of modifications carried out on our wblock **block01.dwg**. As can be seen in some of the examples given in Fig. 7.6, care must be exercised when scaling X and Y to different settings if distortion of the block is to be avoided. If the **Stretch** tool is used, the block must first be acted upon by **Explode**.

Libraries of symbols

Libraries of symbols in the form of AutoCAD drawing files can either be purchased from specialist firms or made up by the operator. Such libraries are designed for constructing drawings such as circuit diagrams, for adding symbols to engineering drawings or to building drawings, or in some cases for producing graphical effects. Commercially available libraries on disks may contain hundreds of symbols. For example the appropriate British Standard for electronics and electrical symbols (BS: 3939 *Graphical symbols for electrical power,*

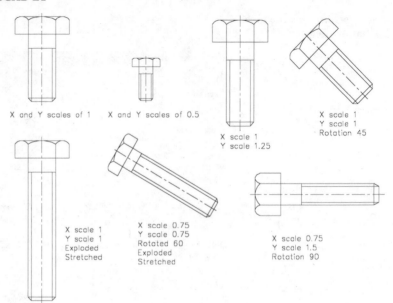

Fig. 7.6 Some examples of
Modify tools used on a wblock

telecommunications and electronics diagrams) contains hundreds of symbols. Disks holding an appropriate range of such symbols in drawing files would contain hundreds of files, appropriately named.

Examples of simple symbols libraries for electric/electronic circuits, for bolts, studs and screws, for building drawing symbols and for pneumatics circuits are given in Figures 7.7 to 7.10. These libraries only contain a small number of symbols. They are shown here to give the reader an idea of how the reader can create small libraries from wblocks.

Fig. 7.8 was made up from a number of wblocks which were inserted into the drawing. With the drawing on screen, if the **Insert** dialogue box is now called (*enter* i or *pick* **Insert Block...** from the

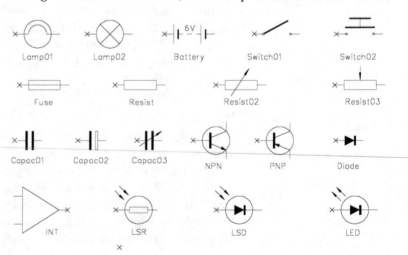

Fig. 7.7 A small library of
electrical and electronics
symbols

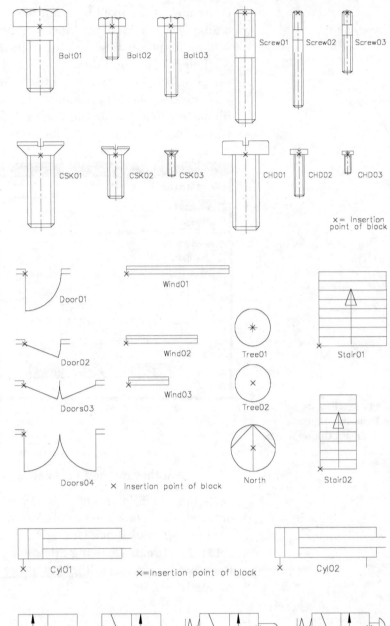

Fig. 7.8 A small library of
bolts, studs and screws

x = Insertion
point of block

Fig. 7.9 A small library of
building drawing symbols

× Insertion point of block

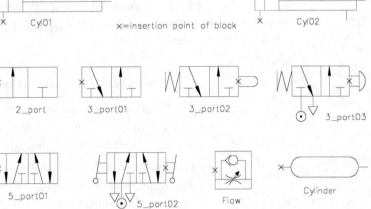

x=Insertion point of block

Fig. 7.10 A small library of
pneumatics symbols

Draw menu) followed by a *left-click* on the **Block...** button in the dialogue box, a list of the blocks in the drawing appears – Fig. 7.11. A *left-click* on the **File...** button in the **Insert** dialogue box brings up the **Select Drawing File** dialogue box, from which drawing file(s) can be selected for inserting into the drawing on screen. When such a drawing is inserted it becomes a block within the drawing and its filename will appear in the **Blocks Defined in the Drawing** dialogue which appears with a *left-click* on the **Blocks...** button.

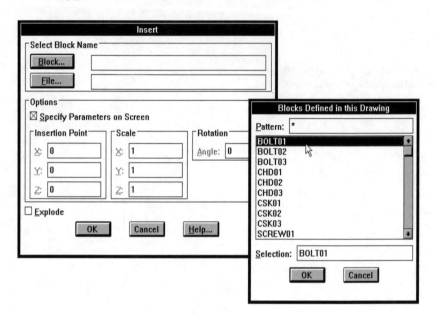

Fig. 7.11 The **Blocks Defined in the Drawing** dialogue box from the **Insert** dialogue box

Another method of creating a wblock

Left-click on **File** in the menu bar. The **File** pull-down menu appears. *Left-click* on **Import/Export** in the menu, followed by another *left-click* **Block Out...** in the sub-menu which appears (Fig. 7.12). The **Create Drawing File** dialogue box appears. Then follow the procedure as for calling **Wblock** by *entering* w at the keyboard as defined on p. 98.

Constructing a circuit diagram from Wblocks

Fig. 7.13 shows the stages in constructing a simple electronics circuit diagram from the symbol drawings shown in Fig. 7.7, which have been saved to a small library on disk. The stages shown are:

1. With the aid of the tool **Insert** insert the required symbols in their approximate positions within the circuit. Do not **Explode** any of the symbols drawings. Rotate those symbols which require to be at an

Fig. 7.12 Calling **Wblock** from
the **File** pull-down menu

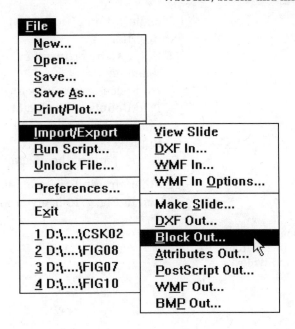

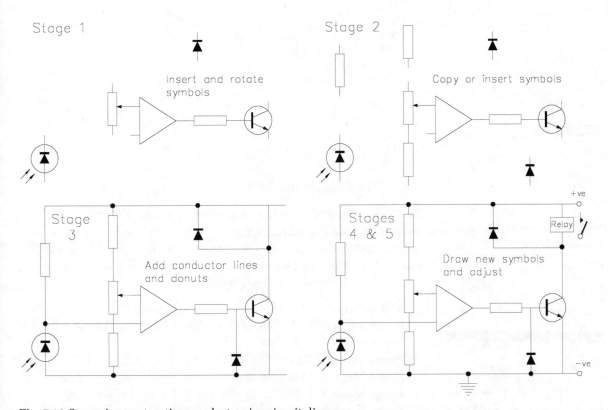

Fig. 7.13 Stages in constructing an electronics circuit diagram

angle different to that at which the symbol was saved during insertion.

2. Either **Copy** or **Insert** symbols which occur in the diagram more than once.
3. Add necessary conductor lines. Use **Osnaps** to ensure accuracy. Add **Donuts** at conductor joins.
4. Construct symbols in the circuit which are not available from the library.
5. Adjust parts of the diagram where necessary.

Another circuit diagram constructed from the pneumatics symbols shown in Fig. 7.10 is given in Fig. 7.14.

Fig. 7.14 A pneumatics ciruit diagram constructed from previously saved **Wblocks**

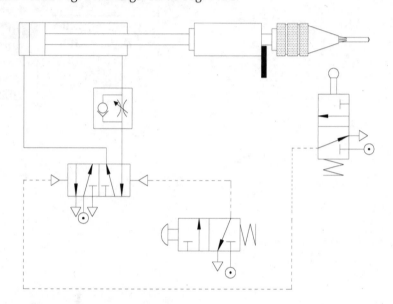

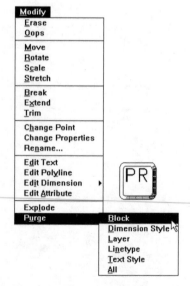

Fig. 7.15 The command **Purge**

The command PURGE

Blocks within drawings inevitably take up some disk space. If those parts of a drawing which are blocks are **Exploded**, the space they occupy in the drawing can be deleted with the aid of the command **Purge**. First the blocks must be acted upon by **Explode**, otherwise they cannot be purged from the file.

Command: *enter* pr (for Purge) *right-click*
Purge unused blocks/Dimstyles/LAyers/LTypes/STyles/All: *enter*
    a (for All) *right-click*
Purge block CYL02 <N>: *enter* y (for Yes) *right-click*
Purge block 3_PORT03 <N>: *enter* y (for Yes) *right-click*
Purge block 5_PORT01<N>: *enter* y (for Yes) *right-click*
Purge block FLOW<N>: *enter* y (for Yes) *right-click*

No unreferenced shape file found
No unreferenced dimensions styles found
Command:

In the example given – Fig. 7.14 – nearly 3 kilobytes of disk space was saved by first exploding blocks, followed by purging them. Other features can also be purged from drawings as can be seen in Fig. 7.15.

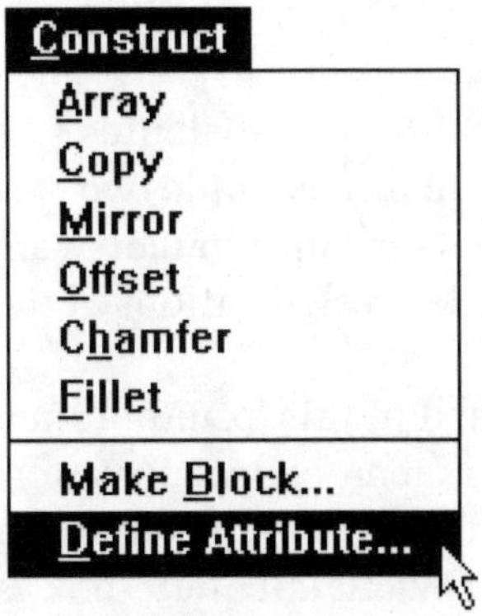

Attributes

Load the symbol drawing 5_port02 from Fig. 7.10. Then *left-click* on **Define Attributes...** in the **Construct** pull-down menu (Fig. 7.16). The **Attribute Definition** dialogue box appears (Fig. 7.17). In the **Attribute Tag** box *enter* description and in the **Attribute Prompt** box *enter* describe. *Left-click* on the **Pick Point<** button, followed by the *picking* of a point just above the loaded pneumatics symbol. The **Attributes Definition** box reappears. *Left-click* on the **OK** button. The word DESCRIPTION (in capital letters) appears above the symbol (Fig. 7.18). Save the symbol and its attribute (DESCRIPTION) as a wblock. Then:

> **Command:** *enter* i (Insert) *right-click*
> In the **Insert** dialogue box select the symbol file (with its attribute)
> **Insertion point:** *pick* **X scale factor <1>:** *right-click*
> **Y scale factor (default=X):** *right-click*
> **Rotation angle <0>:** *right-click*

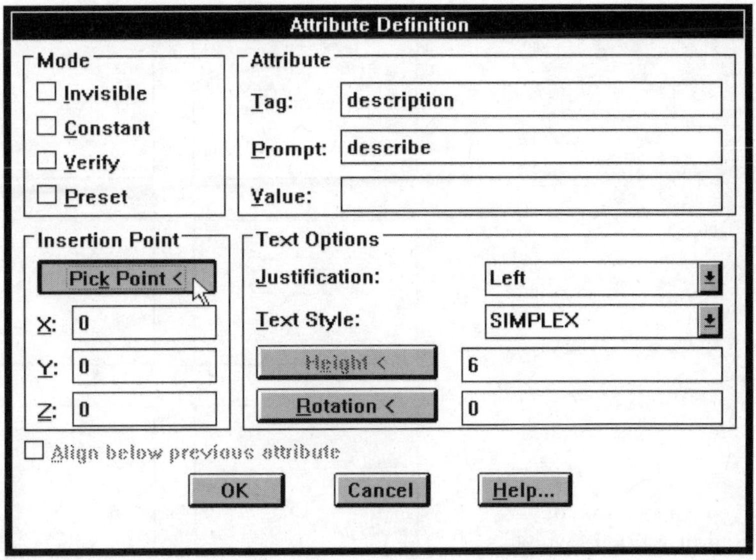

Fig. 7.16 **Define Attributes** from the **Construct** pull-down menu

Fig. 7.17 The **Attribute Definition** dialogue box with entries in the **Tag** and **Prompt** boxes

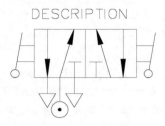

Fig. 7.18 A pneumatics symbol with an **Attribute** tag ready to be saved as a **Wblock**

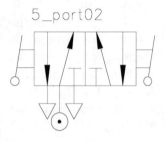

Fig. 7.19 The wblock of Fig. 7.18 with its description added as an attribute

Enter attribute values
describe: *enter* 5_port02 *right-click*
Command:

Note that the prompt **describe:** is that which was entered in the **Attribute Prompt** box of the **Attribute Definition** dialogue box. The resulting attribute 5_port02 appears in its correct position – Fig. 7.19.

Another example of attributes

Fig. 7.20 shows another example of the addition of attributes to a block inserted several times into a drawing. In this example two tags and prompts – **Students name** and **Students group number** were included with the block of the rectangle of the desk positions of the students.

Other attributes could have been included in this example such as the students address, home telephone number, college tutor etc. Each attribute will need to be entered in separate **Attribute Definition** dialogue boxes and, if the **Align below previous attribute** box is checked, the attributes will line up one below the other. Each attribute will have its own prompt appearing in turn one after the other in the command prompt sequence at the command line.

The reader is advised to *left-click* on the **Help** button in the **Attribute Definition** dialogue box and read the help advice about other features in the **Attribute Definition** dialogue box.

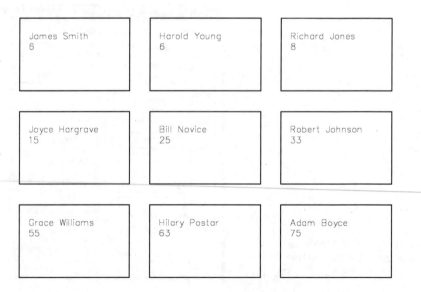

Fig. 7.20 An example of repeated insertion of wblocks with attributes

Questions

1. What is the difference between a wblock and a block?
2. When a wblock is being saved to disk, the drawing being saved as a wblock disappears from the screen. What action must be taken to get the drawing back on screen?
3. When a wblock is inserted into a drawing, how does the block appear on screen?
4. What is the purpose of the tool **Explode**?
5. Which **Modify** tools can be used in relation to an inserted block?
6. How can you find which blocks are already in a drawing on screen?
7. What is the purpose of the tool **Purge**?
8. What is meant by a library of drawing files in relation to working in a CAD system such as AutoCAD LT?
9. What are the main advantages of using wblocks?
10. What is an **Attribute**?

Exercises

1. Fig. 7.21. Draw a sufficient number of symbols selected from Fig. 7.9 and copy the given drawing of the plan of a bungalow. Sizes are left to your own judgement. Fig. 7.22 shows the construction of the bottom right-hand corner of the plan – the double cavity wall can be drawn with the aid of the tool **DLINE**. Frequent use of the

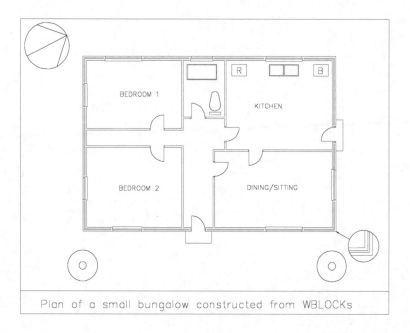

Fig. 7.21 Exercise 1

Plan of a small bungalow constructed from WBLOCKs

tool **TRIM** will be necessary to construct the answer to this exercise.

Fig. 7.22 Detail from the plan
Fig. 7.21

2. Fig. 7.23. Copy sufficient of the electronics symbols from Fig. 7.7. Make a small library of wblocks from your symbols and copy the given circuit. Add details of the components of the circuit as attributes.

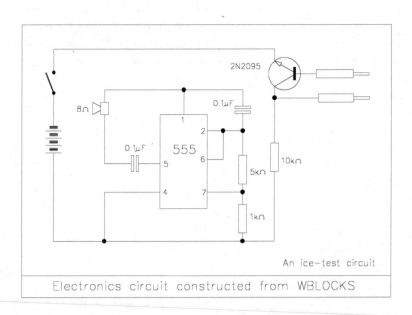

Fig. 7.23 Exercise 2

3. Fig. 7.24 is a circuit diagram for a simple transistor radio. Make a sufficient number of symbol wblocks to construct the circuit and complete the diagram to the details given.

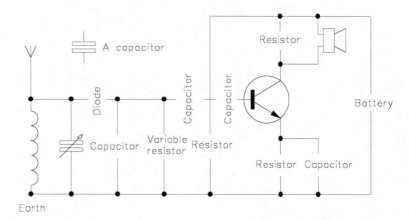

Fig. 7.24 Exercise 3

4. Fig. 7.25 is another electronics circuit diagram. From your previously made up small electronics library copy the given diagram. Add the names of the components in the circuit as attributes.

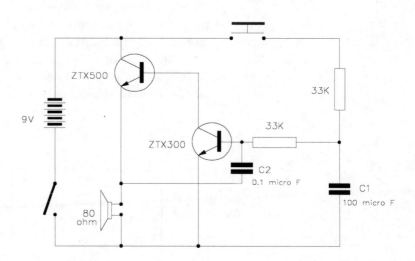

Fig. 7.25 Exercise 4

5. Fig. 7.26 is another building plan of a bungalow. Copy the given plan using symbols from the small library you developed for constructing the answer to Exercise 1.

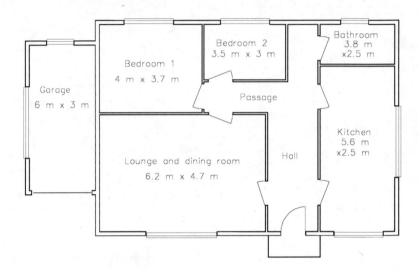

Fig. 7.26 Exercise 5

6. Fig. 7.27 gives the outline only of the building plan of the ground floor of a large two-storey house. Working to a scale of 1:50, using your own judgement about dimensions not included with Fig. 7.27 and including suitably positioned doors and windows construct an accurate copy of the plan. Include the names of the rooms and spaces in the plan and add sizes of the doors and windows as attributes to the blocks drawn to show windows and doors.

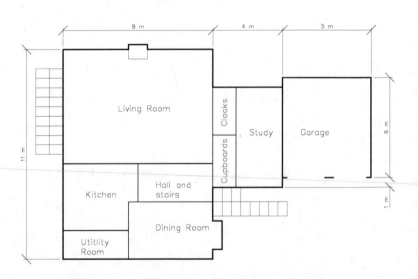

Fig. 7.27 Exercise 6

7. Using Attributes design and construct a series of rectangles similar to those given in Fig. 7.20 showing the following details of 12 friends or acquaintances:
   Surnames and Christian names
   Addresses
   Telephone numbers
   Their place of work or college

CHAPTER 8

Dimensions

Associative dimensioning

Dimensions in AutoCAD LT drawings can be either **Associative** or not. If associative, dimensions – lines, extension lines, arrows and text are treated as a single entity – each part of the dimension is associated with its other parts and the whole can be regarded as a single entity – similar to a block. If not associative, each part of a dimension is a separate entity. **Associative** dimensioning can be set at the command line:

> **Command:** *enter* dimaso *right-click*
> **New value for DIMASO <0>:** *enter* 1 *right-click*
> **Command:**

The setting for associative dimensioning **on** is **Dimaso** = 1.
The setting for associative dimensioning **off** is **Dimaso** = 0.

Another method is to select **Associative Dimensions from** the **Settings** menu – Fig. 8.1. If a tick is present against the name, the associative dimensioning is on. If no tick then it is off. A *left-click* on the name toggles between the tick being present and being absent (on or off).

Settings menu:

- **S**ettings
  - **S**hort Menu
  - **A**erial View
  - Tool**b**ox Style
  - **E**ntity Modes...
  - **D**rawing Aids...
  - **L**ayer Control...
  - Li**n**etype Style ▶
  - **T**ext Style...
  - Di**m**ension Style...
  - ✓ Associati**v**e Dimensions
  - **P**olyline Style ▶
  - P**o**int Style...
  - **U**nits Style...
  - **G**rips Style...
  - Sele**c**tion Style...
  - Dra**w**ing ▶

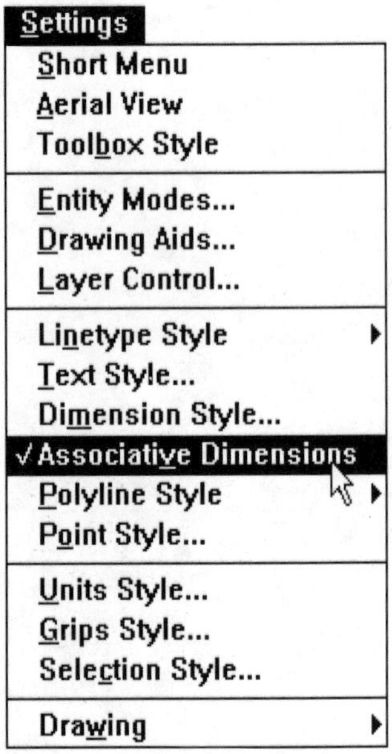

Fig. 8.1 **Associative Dimensions** from the **Settings** pull-down menu

Setting Dimension Styles

The styles for dimensioning – dimension lines, extension lines, arrows and text are set from the **Dimension Styles and Settings** dialogue box, which appears with a *left-click* on **Dimension Style...** in the **Settings** menu (Fig. 8.1). When the dialogue box appears it will be seen that it contains a number of buttons which will bring up further dialogue boxes for the settings of the dimensioning parameters – Fig. 8.2. Figures 8.3 to 8.8 show each of these dialogue boxes in turn with settings suitable for the work in this book.

The settings shown in this series of dialogue boxes are those which the author uses when working in AutoCAD LT with **Limits** set to **420,297** – that is as suitable for plotting or printing full scale on

Plate I The AutoCAD LT graphics window with the **File** pull-down menu

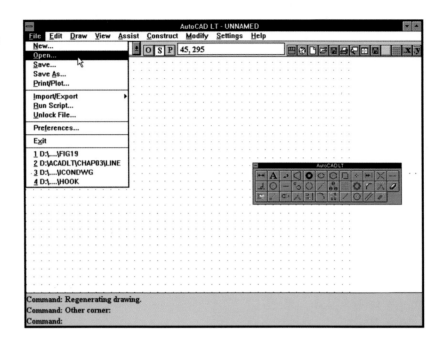

Plate II The **AutoCAD LT Window Colors** window from the **Preferences** dialogue box

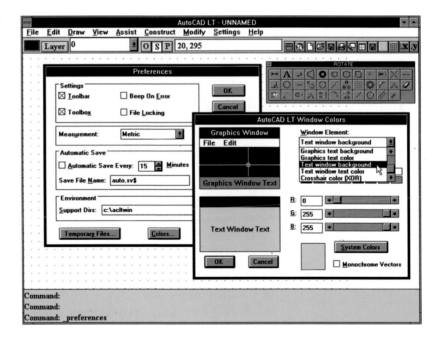

Plate III A 3D solid
model loaded into
AutoCAD LT

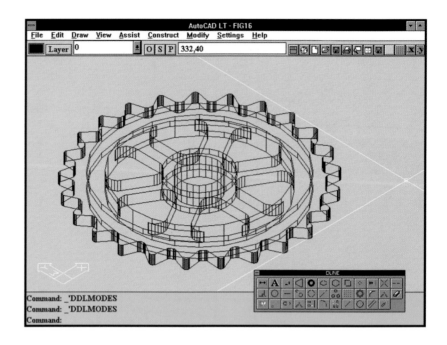

Plate IV A 2D drawing
constructed in a number
of colours within
AutoCAD LT shown
against a black background

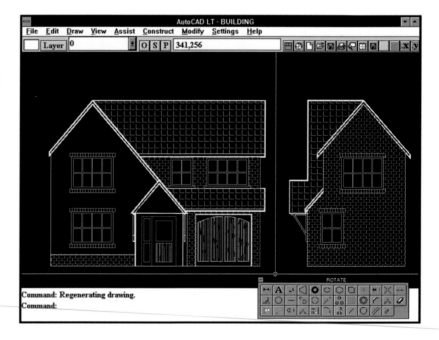

Plate V The same 2D drawing as in Plate IV shown against a white background

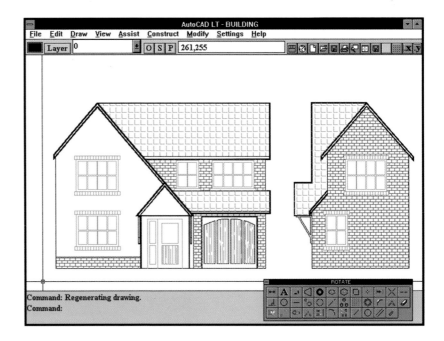

Plate VI The **Change System Settings** window from **Windows Setup** within **Program Manager**

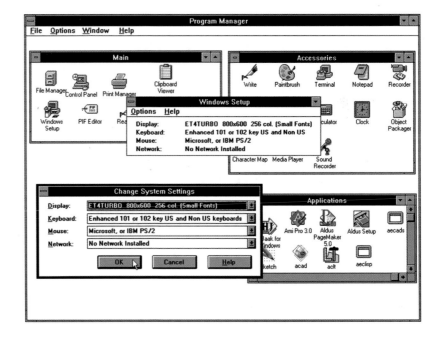

Plate VII The **Color**
window from the
Windows **Control Panel**

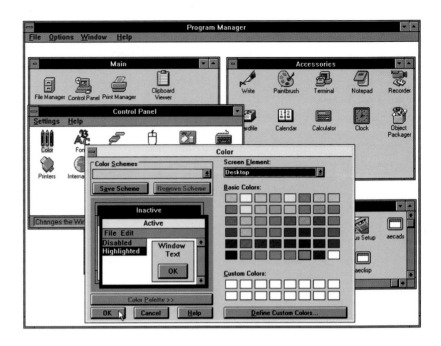

Plate VIII The first of the
Select Hatch Pattern
dialogue boxes

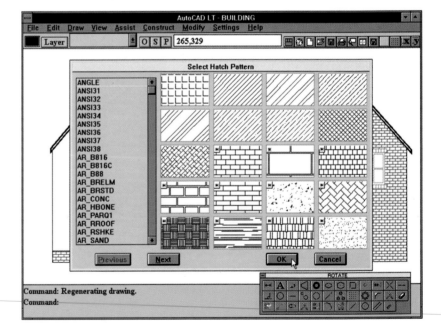

Plate IX The AutoCAD LT **Aerial View** window showing an area in a **Zoom** window

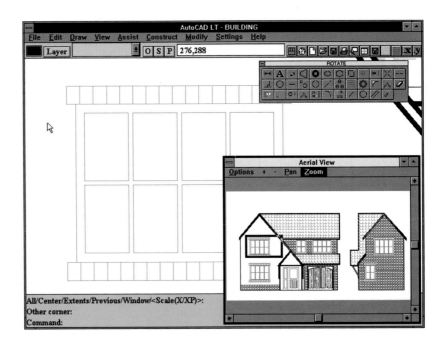

Plate X A **Help** window called while **Zoom** is in operation by pressing the **F1** key

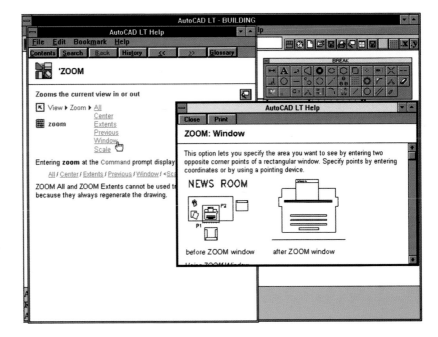

Plate XI The **Import/ Export** sub-menu of the **File** pull-down menu

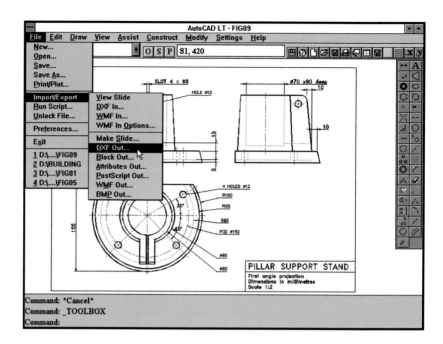

Plate XII A 3D solid model in a four-viewport setup in **Model Space**

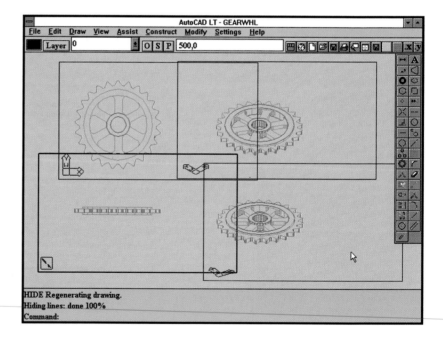

Plate XIII The same four-viewport setup as Plate XII in **Paper Space**

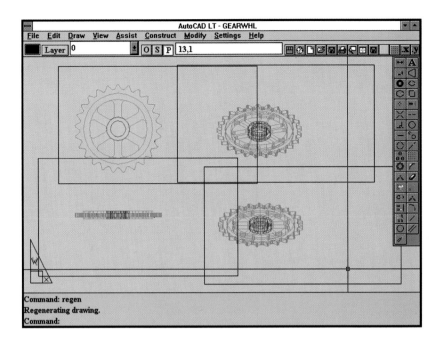

Plate XIV A 3D solid model in AutoCAD LT with the **3D Viewpoint Presets** sub-menu of the **View** menu

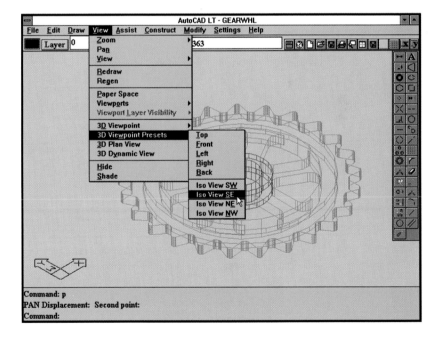

Plate XV The Windows **Clipboard Viewer** showing against a drawing linked by **Copy Link**

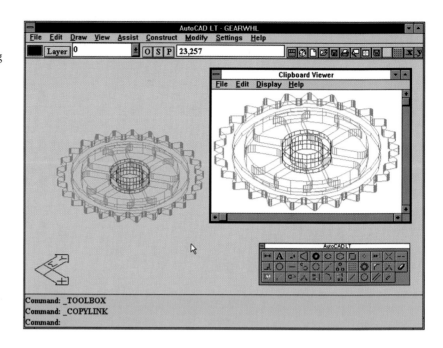

Plate XVI The AutoCAD LT **Toolbox Customization** dialogue box

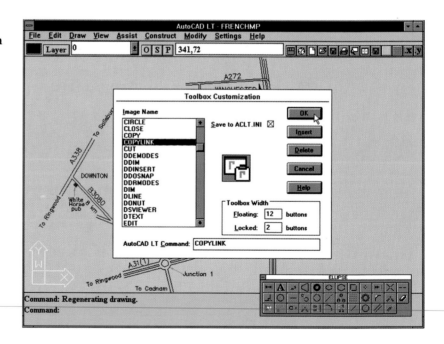

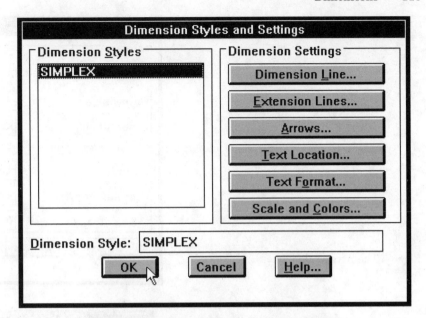

Fig. 8.2 The **Dimension Styles and Settings** dialogue box

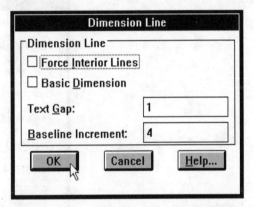

Fig. 8.3 The **Dimension Line** dialogue box

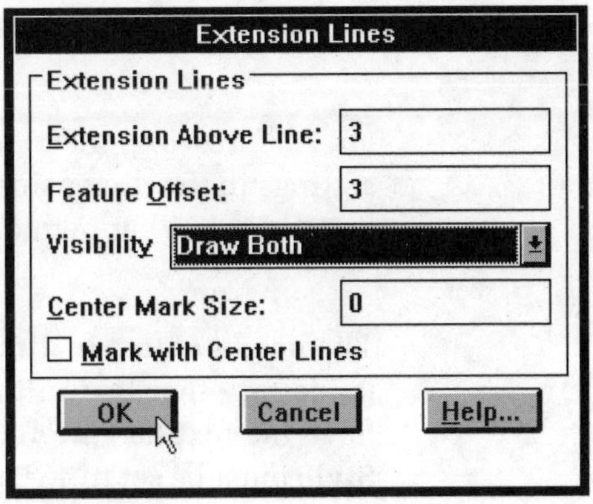

Fig. 8.4 The **Extension Lines** dialogue box

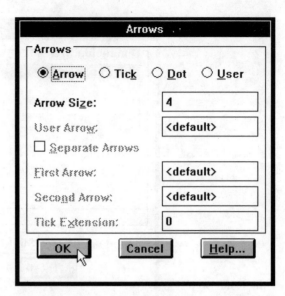

Fig. 8.5 The **Arrows** dialogue box

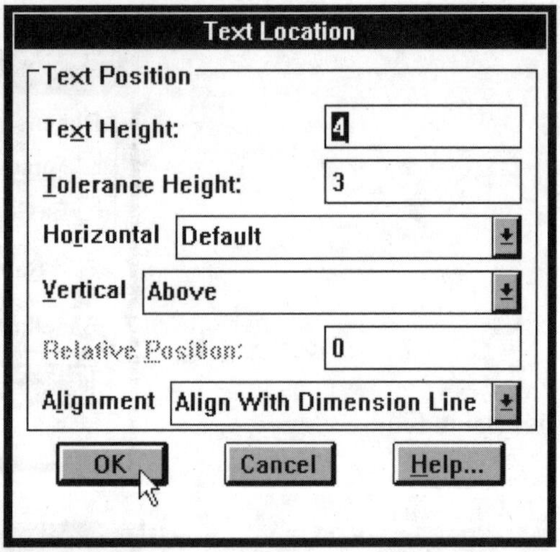

Fig. 8.6 The **Text Location** dialogue box

an A3 drawing sheet. The reader should experiment with the settings in the dimension settings dialogue boxes to find those best suited for his/her own drawing style.

Note

The height of text in dimensions is determined by the **Style** setting made for other text in the current drawing. Thus if one wishes to have the text height of a dimension set to 4 high, the current font **Style** must be set to 4. The exception to this is if the current style is **Standard** (txt.shx) set to a smaller height than the setting in the **Text Location** dialogue box.

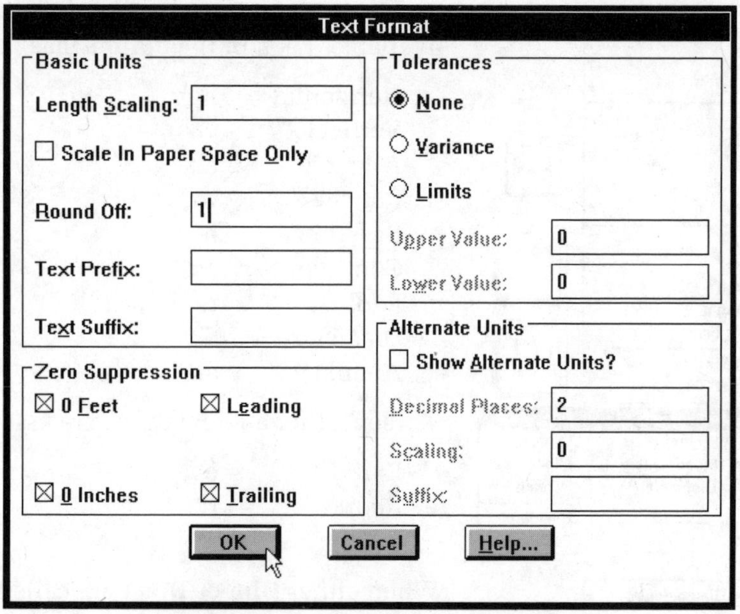

Fig. 8.7 The **Text Format**
dialogue box

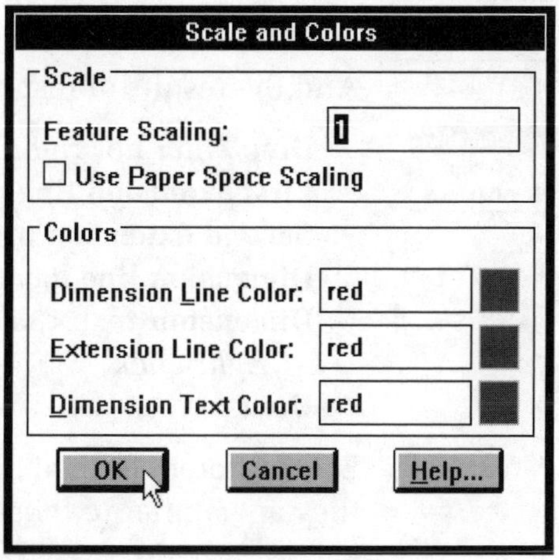

Fig. 8.8 The **Scale and Colors**
dialogue box

Including dimensions in a drawing

There are two dimensioning tools – **Dim** and **Dim1**. If **Dim** is called,
dimensions can be placed in a drawing one after the other without
recalling **Dim**. If **Dim1** is called only a single dimension of any kind
can be placed, after which **Dim1** has to be called again if further
dimensions are required. All dimensions calls made by selecting
options from the **draw** pull-down menu are of the **Dim1** type. The
abbreviation for **Dim** is d, the abbreviation for **Dim1** is d1 – Fig. 8.9.
The dimensioning options from the **Draw** pull-down menu are all of
the **Dim1** type.

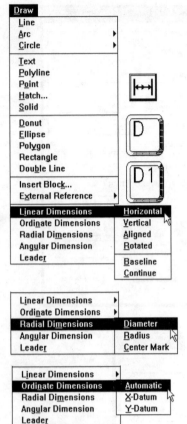

Fig. 8.9 shows the variety of different forms of dimensioning available. Each of the options has its own abbreviation:

Horizontal	hor
Vertical	ve
Aligned	al
Rotated	ro
Baseline	b
Continue	co
Radius	ra
Diameter	d
Angular	an

Three further abbreviations are associated with **Dim** or **Dim1**:

Exit	e
Redraw	r
Zoom	z

When either **Dim** or **Dim1** are called, the command line shows:

Command: *enter* d *right-click*
Dim:

And the results of responses produce further prompts:

Dim: *enter* hor *right-click*
First extension line origin or RETURN to select: *pick*
Second extension origin: *pick*
Dimension line location (Text/Angle): *pick*
Dimension text <35>: either *right-click* to accept or *enter* text
  right-click
Dim:

Fig. 8.9 Calling the various
Dim options

Each different form of dimensioning has its own set of prompts, but they are similar to those for the horizontal option.

Examples of dimensions in drawings

Fig. 8.10 shows the types of dimensions which are most likely to occur in drawing. The prompts associated with vertical (ve) dimensions are similar to those for horizontal (hor) ones. The prompts for radial (ra) and diameter (d) dimensions follow the pattern:

Command: *enter* d *right-click*
Select arc or circle: *pick*
Dimension text <160>: *right-click* to accept or *enter* text *right-click*
Enter leader length for text: *pick* or *enter* length *right-click*
Dim:

The dimension is entered prefixed by **R** if a radius or prefixed by the symbol⌀ if a diameter. If a different radius or diameter to the default one is required the new text must be entered prefixed by **R** if a radius or by **%%C** if a diameter.

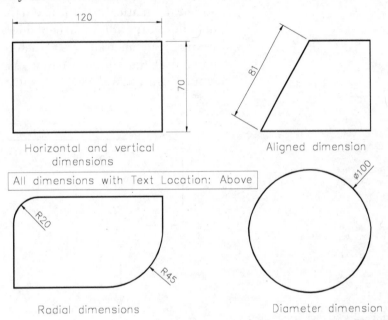

Fig. 8.10 Examples of dimensions

Baseline and Continue dimensions

Fig. 8.11 shows the results of using the responses Baseline (b) and Continue (c) and Angular (an). For the examples in this illustration amendments have been made in the **Text Location** dialogue box (Fig. 8.6) in the **Horizontal** and **Vertical** boxes of the dialogue box to force text inside and relative to the dimension line.

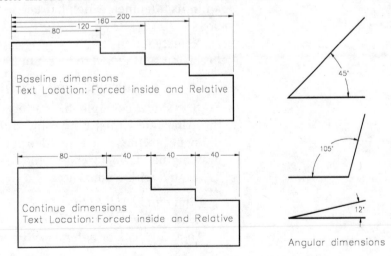

Fig. 8.11 Further examples of dimensions

Dimensions which include tolerances

Fig. 8.12 shows an outline with toleranced dimensions. The tolerances were set to **Variance** and with **Upper** and **Lower Values** set to 0.05 in the **Text Format** dialogue box (Fig. 8.7). The = and ∠ symbols are added automatically to the text if the default figure is accepted. If the default figures are not acceptable and the ± symbol is required in front of a tolerance *enter* **%%p** before the tolerance. Thus **80%%p0.05** entered at the command line in place of the default dimension would result in **80±0.05** in the dimension.

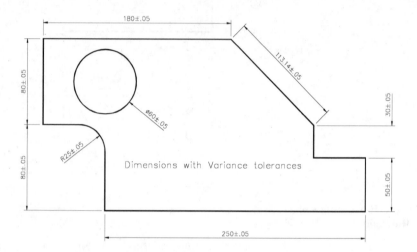

Fig. 8.12 Variance tolerance dimensions

A similar problem arises if the default angle of an angular dimension is not acceptable. In this case *entering* **60%%d** in response to the prompt **Dimension text <45>:** would result in **60°** appearing with the dimension. Fig. 8.13 includes a drawing dimensioned with a **Limits** tolerance which has been set in the **Text Format** dialogue box.

Note that in the tolerancing examples given here, the **Units Style Precision** setting had to be set to 2 figures after the decimal point.

Alternate units, Prefix, Suffix and Leaders

Fig 8.13 shows examples of a variety of types of dimensions in which the **Alternate Units**, **Prefix** and **Suffix** boxes in the **Text Format** dialogue box have been added to or checked. The bottom right-hand drawing of Fig. 8.13 shows the use of Leaders (l). The prompts associated with leaders are:

Dim: *enter* l *right-click*
Leader start: *pick* or *enter* coordinates
To point: *pick* or *enter* coordinates

Dimension text: *enter* required text *right-click*
Dim:

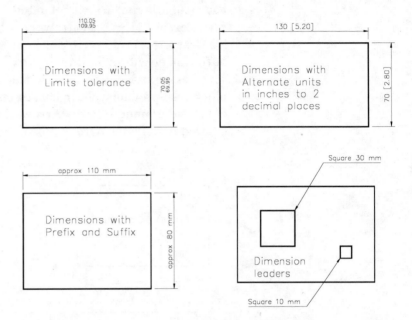

Fig. 8.13 Other types of
dimensioning

The effects of Scale and Stretch on dimensions

Fig. 8.14 shows the results of these two tools on outlines dimensioned
with **Associative Dimensions** on. The dimensions adapt to the
different sizes caused by the actions of the two tools. If **Associative
Dimensions** is off the dimensions do not change.

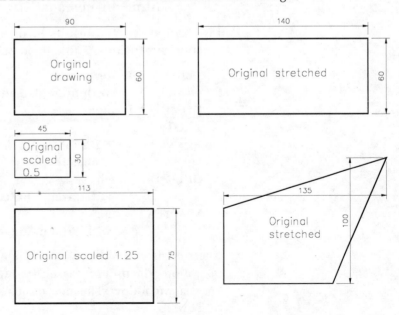

Fig. 8.14 The effects of **Scale**
and **Stretch** on **Associative**
dimensions

Arrows

Fig. 8.15 shows a number of outlines in which the added dimensions have had different arrows set in the **Arrows** dialogue box (Fig. 8.5). In this example two **User** arrows have been included in the drawings. If a **User** arrow is required, a one unit size drawing of the arrow must be first made within the drawing in which the arrow is to be used and saved as a block with a specific name. In Fig. 8.15 two **User** arrow blocks had previously been constructed and saved as blocks named **cross** and **diamond**. In the **Arrow** dialogue box, these names were entered in the **User Arrow:** box of the dialogue box.

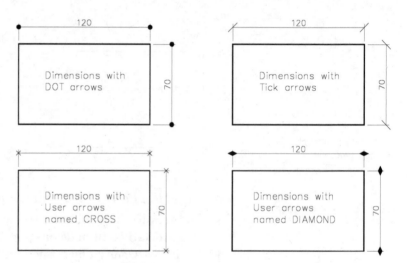

Fig. 8.15 Dimensions with various types of **Arrows**

Editing dimensions

Fig. 8.16 shows the results of using dimension editing tools on existing dimensions. These tools, with their abbreviations, are:

TEDIT	**te**
	with prompts **Left/Right/Home/Angle**
HOMETEXT	**hom**
TROTRATE	**tr**
	with prompts **Enter text angle:** and **Select objects:**
OBLIQUE	**ob**
	with prompt **Enter obliquing angle:**
NEWTEXT	**ne**
	with Prompt **Enter new text:**

These tools can only be used when the **Dim** tool (or **Dim1**) is in operation. The prompts associated with this set of editing tools are very easy to follow. The most often used of these tools will probably be **TEDIT**.

Transparent commands with DIM

Two tools (command) **Redraw** and **Zoom** can be used while in **Dim** or **Dim1**. The two tools produce prompts and act as they would do outside the use of the two dimensioning tools.

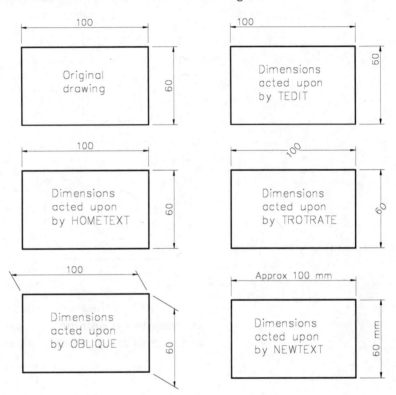

Fig. 8.16 Examples of methods of editing dimensions

Questions

1. What is the function of the variable DIMASO?
2. What is meant by Associative dimensioning?
3. How are the parameters for dimensions set in AutoCAD LT?
4. How is the height of text for dimensions set?
5. What happens when you *enter* %%c50 for a dimension when using the Dim tool?
6. What happens when you *enter* %%p0.5 for a dimension when using the Dim tool?
7. What are the abbreviations for: Horizontal? Vertical? Aligned? Radius? Diameter? when using the Dim tool?
8. What is the purpose of the editing tool TEDIT?
9. What is the difference between entering dimensions with Dim and with Dim1?
10. What differences would you expect if you were entering tolerances with **Variance** set as against **Limits** set?

Exercises

1. Fig. 8.17. Using **PLINE** with width set to 0.7, copy the four outlines of Fig. 8.17 and fully dimensions them.

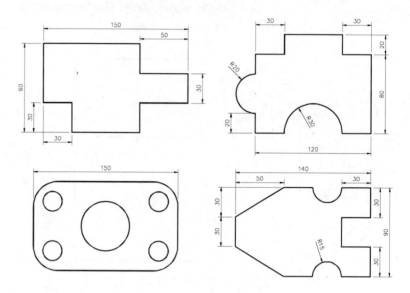

Fig. 8.17 Exercise 1

2. Fig. 8.18. Copy the given outlines and fully dimension them. For Drawing 1 use **Continue**; for 2 use **Baseline**; for 3 use any suitable angles; for Drawing 4 include tolerances of ± 0.05.

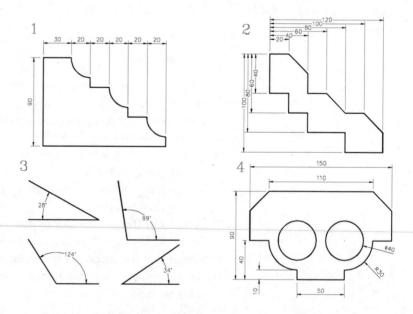

Fig. 8.18 Exercise 2

CHAPTER 9

Orthographic projections

Introduction

In the engineering and building industries, the majority of drawings are orthographic projections. This form of projection is a two-dimensional (2D) method of representing three-dimensional (3D) objects by looking at the object being drawn from a variety of directions and drawing what is seen as if sighting lines are parallel to each other. Perspective is ignored.

The object to be drawn is placed in one of the quadrants formed by two imaginary planes at right angles to each other – a Vertical Plane (V.P.) and a Horizontal Plane (H.P.). Of the four quadrants formed by these two imaginary crossing planes, only two are of any

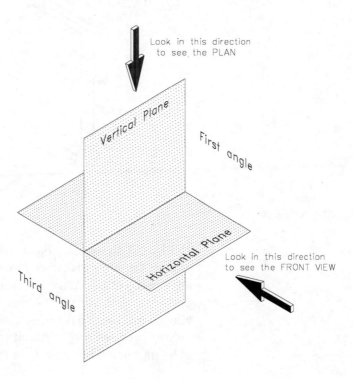

Fig. 9.1 The basis of orthographic projection

value for the production of orthographic projections – the First and the Third angles. Fig. 9.1 shows the setup for the two orthogonal planes. The word *orthogonal* has the same meaning as 'at right angles' – hence the term orthographic – literally graphics from orthogonal planes. Note the directions in which viewing takes place to see two of the main views – FRONT VIEW and PLAN – of any orthographic projection.

First and Third angle orthographic projections

Fig. 9.2 shows an object placed in the First angle of the two orthogonal planes. The object is viewed from the front and what is seen is projected onto the V.P. to produce the FRONT VIEW. The object is viewed from above and what is seen is projected onto the H.P. – the PLAN.

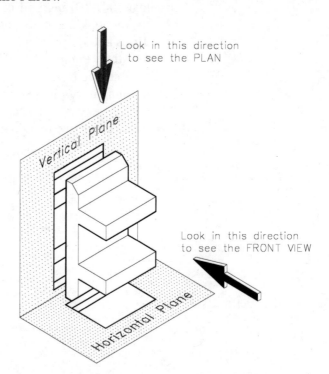

Fig. 9.2 The basis of First angle orthographic projection

Fig. 9.3 shows an object placed in the Third angle of the two planes. The object is viewed from the same directions as for the First angle projection. What is seen when viewed from the front is projected onto the V.P. – the FRONT VIEW. What is seen when viewed from above is projected onto the H.P. – the PLAN. When the views have been projected onto the planes, the V.P. is then imagined as being rotated backwards in line with the H.P. The results of this

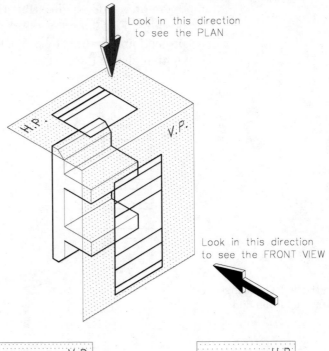

Look in this direction
to see the PLAN

H.P.

V.P.

Look in this direction
to see the FRONT VIEW

Fig. 9.3 The basis of Third
angle orthographic projection

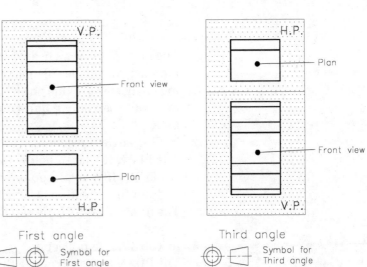

V.P.

Front view

Plan

H.P.

First angle

Symbol for
First angle

H.P.

Plan

Front view

V.P.

Third angle

Symbol for
Third angle

Fig. 9.4 First and Third angle
orthographic projections
compared

rotation for both First and Third angle projections is shown in Fig.
9.4. Included in Fig. 9.4 are the two symbols for showing whether an
orthographic projection is in First or Third angle. The symbols are
truncated cones, themselves drawn in the appropriate angles.

Other views in orthographic projections

The idea of projecting onto either V.Ps or H.Ps can be carried a stage
further to produce further views – in fact as many views as the

operator needs to describe the object being drawn as fully as possible. Fig. 9.5 shows end views in both First and Third angle projections obtained by projections on to a second imaginary V.P. at right angles to the first.

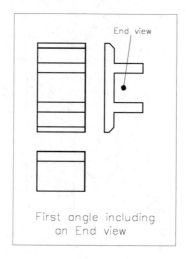 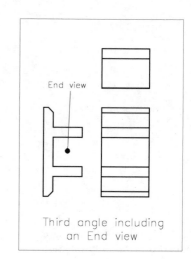

Fig. 9.5 First and Third angle projections including End views

Notes

1. The number of views in an orthographic projection is governed by the need to describe a 3D object as fully as possible without drawing too many views. Some objects, such as those made from thin plate materials may only require one view. Others may require two or more.
2. In First angle projection:
    The **PLAN** is placed below the front view.
    An **END VIEW** is placed on the opposite side of the Front view from the direction at which it was viewed.
    The fronts of both **PLAN** and **END VIEW** face away from the Front view.
3. In Third Angle projection:
    The **PLAN** is placed above the Front view.
    An **END VIEW** is placed on the same side of the Front view as the object was viewed from.
    The fronts of both **PLAN** and **END VIEW** face towards the Front view.
4. The term *elevation* is often used in place of the term *view*.

Lines in engineering drawings

Fig. 9.6 shows the types of line used for constructing engineering drawings in orthographic projections.

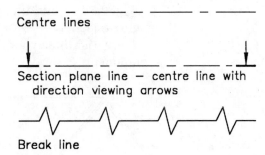

Outlines — 0.7 mm thick

This lines — 0.3 mm thick:
    dimension lines, hatch lines,
    projection lines

Hidden detail lines

Centre lines

Section plane line — centre line with
    direction viewing arrows

Break line

Fig. 9.6 Types of lines used in orthographic engineering drawings

Hidden detail – for lines that cannot be seen from the outside of a view, but which show details hidden from the outside view.

Centre lines – all arcs circles and cylindrical features should have centre lines drawn along their axes.

Section plane lines – are drawn showing the edge of the plane that cuts through an object to produce a sectional view (see Chapter 10).

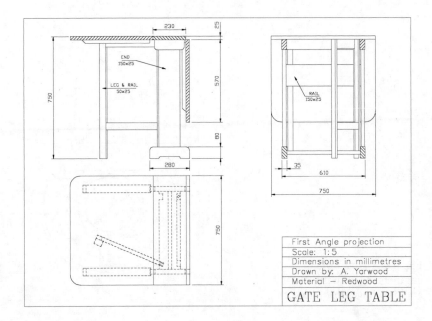

Fig. 9.7 An example of a First angle orthographic projection – a working drawing of a gate leg table

Break lines – occur where a view is broken – usually to allow both ends of a view to be drawn in a smaller area than the whole view would require.

Some examples of orthographic projections

Fig. 9.7 is a First angle orthographic projection of a piece of furniture – a gate leg table. This type of drawing is often referred to as a *working drawing* because the item can largely be made from the description of the item from the drawing.

Fig. 9.8 is a building drawing – Front and End views in Third angle projection.

Fig. 9.9 is a three-view First angle projection of a simple engineering component.

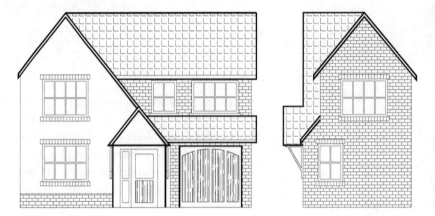

Fig. 9.8 An example of a Third angle orthographic projection - two views of a building

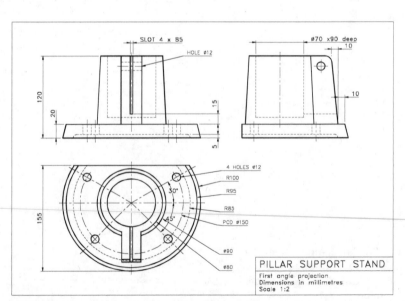

Fig. 9.9 An example of an engineering drawing in First angle orthographic projection

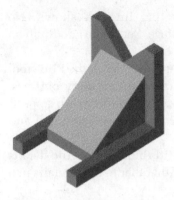

Fig. 9.10 A block from which a First angle projection is to be constructed

All three of these example drawings were constructed in AutoCAD LT. These three examples are typical of the type of draughting/design work for which the software is so well suited.

Constructing a First angle orthographic projection

To construct a three-view (Front, Plan and End) First angle orthographic projection of the block shown in Fig. 9.10:

Set up layers as shown in Fig. 9.11 and with **Limits** set to 420,297 (A3).

Stage 1 With layer **CONSTRUCT** current, draw the three view outlines as in Fig. 9.12. Set **ORTHO** on for this (press the **F8** key). The dimensions should not be included. They are included in Fig. 9.12 to assist you;

Fig. 9.11 The layer setup for the specimen orthographic projection

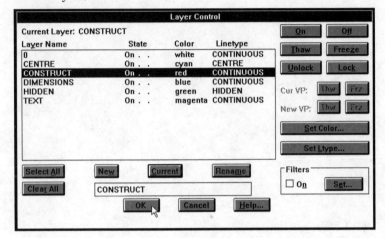

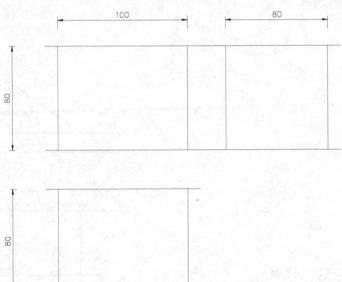

Fig. 9.12 Stage 1 of the construction

Stage 2 Fig. 9.13. Add other construction lines as shown. No dimensions need be included at this stage. Set **Ortho** and **Snap** on (**F8** and **F9**).

Stage 3 Fig. 9.14. Set Layer **0** as the current layer. With the **Pline** tool drawing polylines to width of 0.7 draw the necessary outlines. Then turn Layer **CONSTRUCT** off. The construction lines disappear.

Stage 4 Fig. 9.15. Make Layer **HIDDEN** the current layer and add hidden detail. Add dimensions.

Stage 5 (final) Fig. 9.16. Add border and title block lines. Add details to the title block in text 8 units high. Add other textual details in 6 units high text.

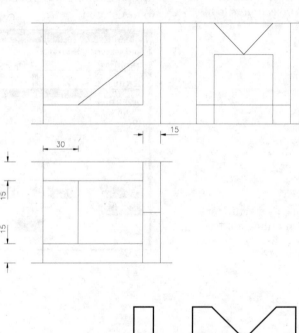

Fig. 9. 13 Stage 2 of the construction

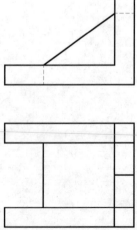

Fig. 9.14 Stage 3 of the construction

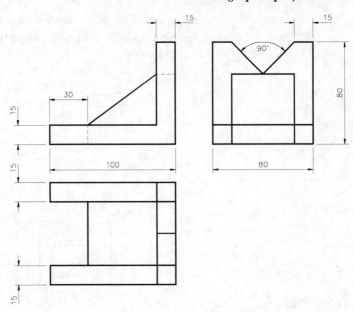

Fig. 9.15 Stage 4 of the construction

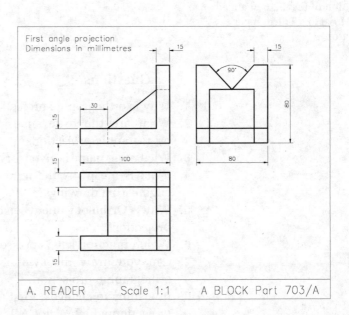

Fig., 9.16 Stage 5 (final) of the construction

If desired, the symbol for First angle projection (Fig. 9.4) could have been drawn in place of the words **First angle projection**. Some draughtsmen may use both.

Changing a First to a Third angle projection

By making use of the **MOVE** tool and with **ORTHO** on (**F8**) a First angle projection can be easily changed to a Third angle projection if required. Fig. 9.17 shows the First angle drawing of Fig. 9.16 changed to a Third angle projection in Fig. 9.17 with the aid of the tool **Move**.

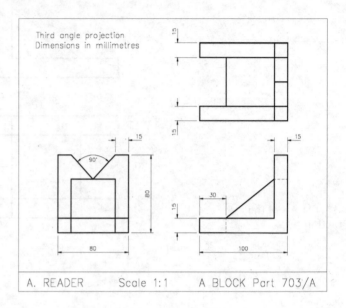

Fig. 9.17 The First angle projection of Fig. 9.16 changed with **Move** to a Third angle projection

Questions

1. Why is orthographic projection given its name?
2. What are the differences between First and Third angle orthographic projections?
3. What other name is given for a 'view' in orthographic projection?
4. What is meant by the term 'Outline line' in connection with engineering drawings?
5. Why is **Ortho** of value when constructing views in orthographic projection?
6. Which function key is pressed to toggle **Snap** on and off?
7. Can you draw the symbol which represents a First angle orthographic projection?
8. If wishing to change a First angle projection into a Third angle projection which AutoCAD LT tool are you most likely to use?
9. Do you know why the second and fourth angles are not used in orthographic projection?
10. What is meant by the term 'orthogonal'?

Exercises

Figures 9.18 to 9.21 for Exercises 1 to 4 are pictorial drawings of engineering components constructed on grids with lines spaced at

10 units apart. The sizes of the various parts of the components are found by counting along the spaces between the lines and multiplying by a factor of 10.

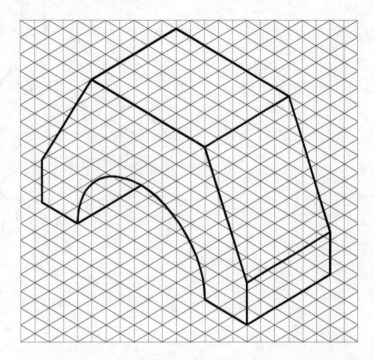

Fig. 9.18 Exercise 1

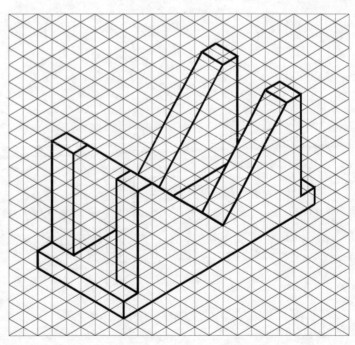

Fig. 9.19 Exercise 2

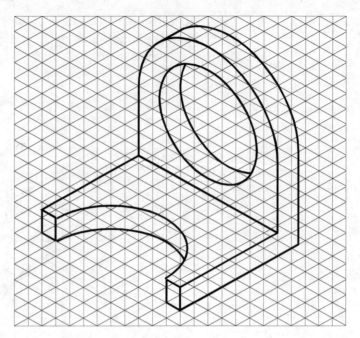

Fig. 9.20 Exercise 3

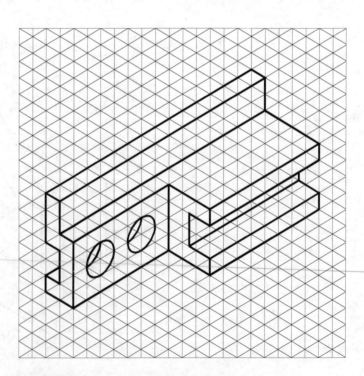

Fig.. 9.21 Exercise 4

1. Fig. 9.18. Construct a three-view First angle projection of the part. Include all necessary dimensions.
2. Fig. 9.19. Construct a three-view Third angle projection of the V-Block including all necessary dimensions. Include all necessary hidden detail.
3. Fig. 9.20. Construct a three-view Third angle projection of the given bracket, including all necessary dimensions. Include all necessary hidden detail.
4. Fig. 9.21. A pictorial view of a slide is given. Construct a three-view First angle projection of the slide. Add all dimensions. Include all necessary hidden detail and centre lines.
5. Fig. 9.22 is a photograph of a Bracket. Fig. 9.23 is a dimensioned Front view of the bracket. The depth from front to back of the lower part of the bracket is 15 units and the depth of the upper part is 5 units. Copy the given Front view and add an End view as seen from the left and a Plan. Work in Third angle projection. Include all necessary centre lines and hidden detail.

Fig. 9.22 A Bracket

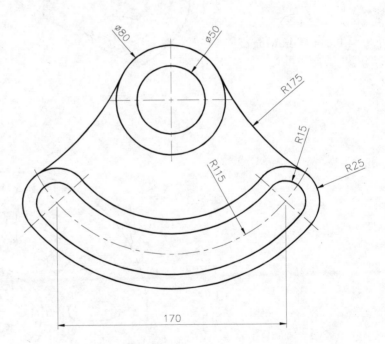

Fig. 9.23 Exercise 5

6. Fig. 9.24 is a pictorial drawing of a Faceplate from an engineering lathe. Fig. 9.25 is a dimensioned Front view of the Faceplate. Copy the given Front view and add an End view in Third angle projection as viewed from the right. Add all necessary dimensions, centre lines and hidden detail. Include a suitable title block with your drawing. Note: Use Polar Array for positioning the slots in the Front view.

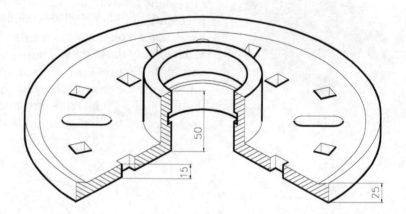

Fig. 9.24 Pictorial drawing of a Faceplate

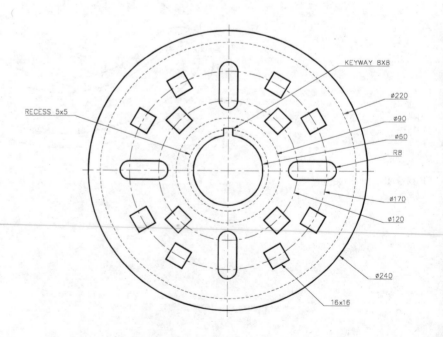

Fig. 9.25 Exercise 6

7. Fig. 9.26 is a photograph of a Pin Slide. Fig. 9.27 is a dimensioned Front view of the slide. Copy the given Front view and add an End view and a Plan in Third Angle projection. Include all dimensions, centre and hidden detail lines and add a suitable title block to your drawing.

Fig. 9.26 A Pin Slide

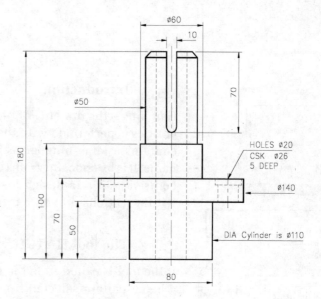

Fig. 9.27 Exercise 7

CHAPTER 10

Hatching and sections

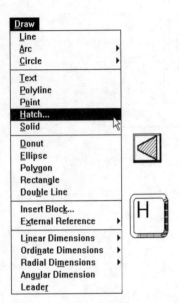

Fig. 10.1 Calling **Hatch**

Introduction

Hatching – the drawing of line patterns within an area enclosed by entities is performed with the aid of the **HATCH** tool. AutoCAD LT contains a large number of hatching patterns, each with its own name. It is by choosing from this variety of patterns that hatching can be used both as a design feature and for including hatching lines within sections drawn in orthographic projections.

The tool HATCH

If the tool is called from the **Draw** pull-down menu (Fig. 10.1) and a hatch pattern selected from the dialogue boxes which appear, a different set of prompts appears at the command line compared to when the tool is called by *entering* the abbreviation h (for Hatch).

Selecting Hatch... from the Draw menu

This results in the first of three dialogue boxes showing the hatch patterns available in pictorial form – the three **Select Hatch Pattern** dialogue boxes appear one after the other with *left-clicks* on the **Next** button in the dialogue box – Figures 10.2 to 10.4. When one of the patterns is selected with a *left-click* on the pattern, followed by a *left-click* on the **OK** button, the command line shows:

> **Command:_hatch**
> **Pattern (? or name/U,style)<u> ansi31**
> **Scale for pattern <1.0000>:** *enter* required scale *right-click*
> **Angle for pattern:** *enter* required angle
> **Select objects:** *pick* all objects of enclosing area in turn
> **Command:**

Calling Hatch from the command line

When an h is *entered* at the keyboard, the command line shows:

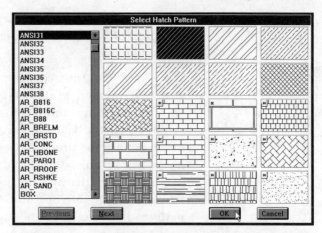

Fig. 10.2 The first of the three **Select Hatch Pattern** dialogue boxes

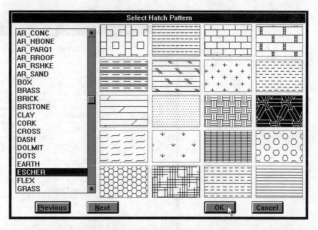

Fig. 10.3 The second of the three **Select Hatch Pattern** dialogue boxes

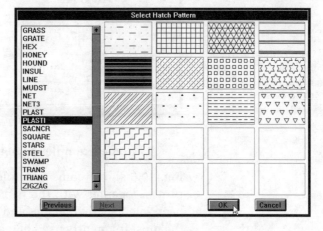

Fig. 10.4 The third of the three **Select Hatch Pattern** dialogue boxes

Command: *enter* h (for Hatch) *right-click*
Pattern (? or name/U, style): *enter* u *right-click*
Angle for cross hatch lines: *enter* a figure *right-click*
Spacing between hatch lines: *enter* a figure *right-click*

Double hatch area?<N>: *right-click* (to accept)
Select objects: *pick* all objects of enclosing area in turn
Command:

If a **?** is *entered* in response to **Pattern (? or name/U, style):** an AutoCAD text screen appears with all the hatch pattern names – Fig. 10.5. Press **F2** and the screen reverts to the AutoCAD LT graphics screen. From the list of names appearing in the text screen, the name of the pattern required can be entered when calling **Hatch** from the keyboard. In order to take advantage of this facility, the operator needs to familiarise him/herself with the names of the hatch patterns which are available in AutoCAD LT, together with what the hatch patterns look like at various spacings and angles.

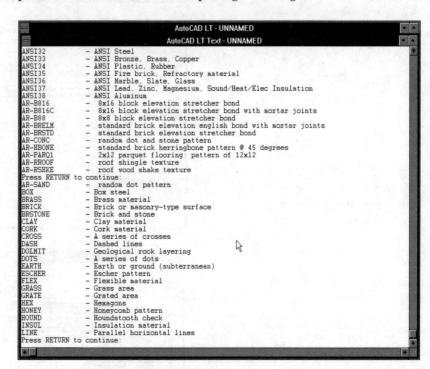

Fig. 10.5 The AutoCAD LT text screen showing the names of all the hatch patterns held in AutoCAD LT

Some examples of hatched areas

Fig. 10.6 shows some examples of areas enclosed by lines, arcs or plines, together with the names of the hatch patterns which have been selected, their angles and their spacings. It should be noted that the most frequently used hatch pattern is probably **ansi31** – used in most hatching of sectional areas in orthographic projections – see Chapter 9. When calling **Hatch** by entering the abbreviation h at the command line (or indeed the full name hatch), in order to obtain ansi31 hatching, it is necessary to respond with u at the prompt

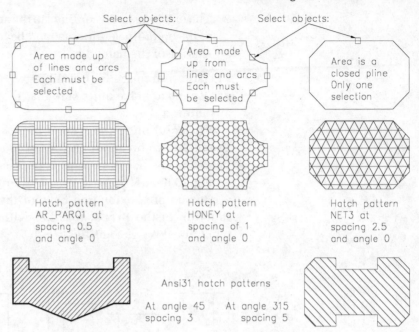

Fig. 10.6 Examples of hatch patterns

Pattern (? or name/U, style):, followed by stating the angle and spacing for the lines of the **ansi31** pattern.

Problems arising when hatching

The main problems which occur when adding hatch patterns to drawings constructed in AutoCAD LT (Fig. 10.7) are:
1. The problem of the hatch pattern showing gaps because of gaps in the bounding area.

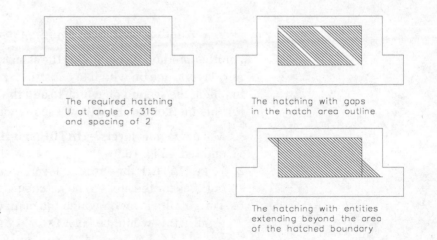

Fig. 10.7 Two problems which may arise when hatching

2. The hatching is not confined to the area to be hatched because some of the bounding entities extend beyond the area. This is known as *leaking* of the hatch lines.

The solution to the first of these two problems is to use **Snap** and/or **Osnaps** to make quite sure that the ends of entities meet exactly as required.

The solution to the second of these two problems is to use the **Break** tool to break all entities at the boundaries of the area to be hatched. The use of **Osnaps** is necessary for this to succeed.

Fig. 10.8 shows how to overcome the problem of entities surrounding a hatched area extending beyond the hatch boundary. Use the **F** function of the **Break**, together with **Osnaps** to ensure accuracy when breaking the entities.

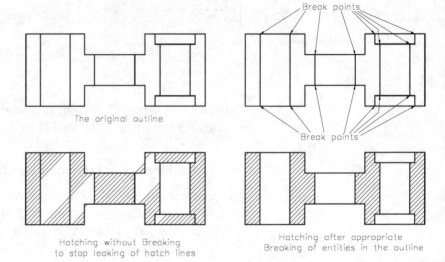

Fig. 10.8 Using the **Break** tool to prevent hatch line leaking

Another method of avoiding leaking

Another method for achieving the same result would be to make two new layers, one on which to construct the outlines of the areas to be hatched, the second on which to add the hatch lines. The procedure for this method could follow a sequence such as:

1. Make two new layers – **HATCH** and **HATCH01** – colours say blue and red – Fig. 10.9.
2. With **HATCH** the current layer, draw lines (or plines) of the outlines for the areas to be hatched.
3. Turn off the layer on which the main outlines have been drawn – usually this would be layer **O**.

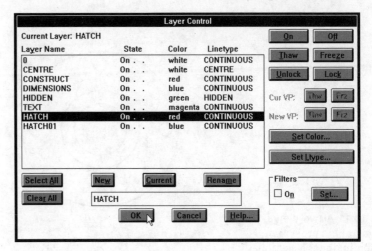

Fig. 10.9 The two new layers **HATCH** and **HATCH01** added in the **Layer Control** dialogue box

4. With **HATCH01** the current layer add the hatch lines inside the hatch area outlines.
5. Turn layer **HATCH** off and make layer **0** the current layer.

The stages in this sequence are illustrated in Fig. 10.10.

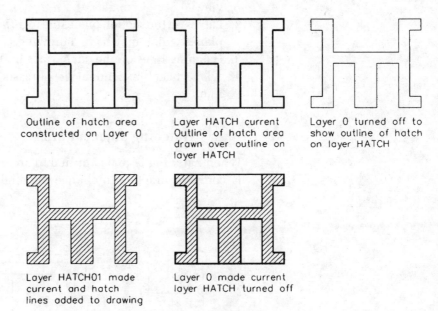

Outline of hatch area constructed on Layer 0

Layer HATCH current Outline of hatch area drawn over outline on layer HATCH

Layer 0 turned off to show outline of hatch on layer HATCH

Layer HATCH01 made current and hatch lines added to drawing

Layer 0 made current layer HATCH turned off

Fig. 10.10 The method of avoiding leaking when hatching by adding two new layers

Sectional view and hatching

Sectional views are of particular importance in orthographic projections because they allow a draughtsman/woman to clearly show the internal shapes within an object – those parts which cannot be seen in an external view. Fig. 10.11 a typical sectional view (often known

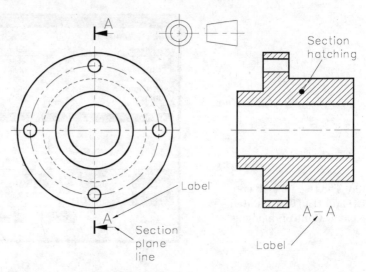

Fig. 10.11 A two-view orthographic projection, which includes a sectional view

as a *section* – i.e. without using the word *view)*. The elements in a sectional view are:

1. A section plane line showing the edge of the imaginary cutting plane which cuts through an object to allow the cut surface to be viewed at right angles.
2. Labels on the section plane line to differentiate it from other cutting planes which may be in a drawing.
3. Hatching lines on the cut surface in the sectional view.
4. A label near the sectional view to associate it with the section plane line.

Hatching adjacent areas

When hatching is to be applied to areas adjacent to one another, it is common practice to change the angle at which the hatching is

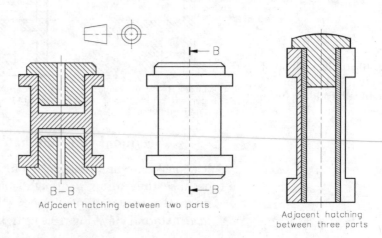

Fig. 10.12 An example of adjacent hatch lines at alternate angles

formed. Fig. 10.12 shows some examples. These examples are taken from engineering drawings where the problem frequently occurs. Note that not only should the lines of adjacent hatched areas be at an alternate angle, but if several hatched areas are adjacent to each other, it may be necessary to change the spacings between the hatch lines as well as the angles.

Different types of sections in engineering drawings

Fig. 10.13 shows a number of different forms of sectional views which may occur within engineering drawings. Those shown are:

Half section – in which the object is symmetrical around a centre line.

Part (or local) section – in which only part of an object requires to be sectioned.

Successive sections – showing sections of different shapes along an object.

Revolved section – in which a section across the object clearly shows its internal shape.

Symmetrical section – in which the sectional view is symmetrical around axes.

Section through thin materials

The main rule to follow when constructing sectional views (sections) is that the meaning of finished view should be quite clear and

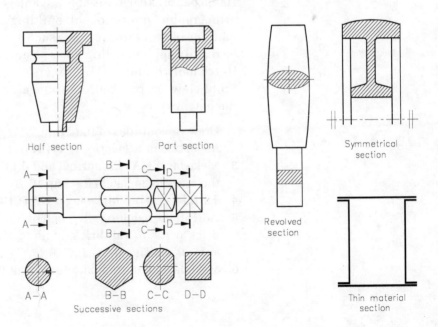

Fig. 10.13 Different types of sectional views

unambiguous, yet, at the same time to be as easy to understand as is possible.

Exceptions to hatching in sectional views

Fig. 10.14 shows some of the parts which, in sectional views, are drawn as outside views. Such outside views are drawn when items such as bolts, nuts, studs, washers, webs, ribs, keys, spindles occur within sections.

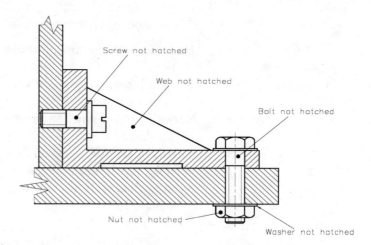

Fig. 10.14 Some examples of exceptions to the rules about hatching in sectional views

Hatching in building drawings

Hatch patterns can be used to advantage when constructing views in orthographic projection of buildings. This is because hatching patterns representing features such as bricks, tiles, concrete etc. can be readily applied within areas of such drawings with the aid of the **Hatch** tool of AutoCAD LT. Figure 10.15 is an example showing the Front view of a two-bedroom bungalow. The sequence for applying the hatching was:

1. Draw the outlines of the Front view on layer **0**.
2. Make two new layers – **HATCH** (red) and **HATCH01** (blue).
3. Make layer **HATCH** current and draw plines along the edges of all the areas to be hatched – Fig. 10.16.
4. Turn layer **0** off. Make layer **HATCH01** current.
5. Add all the hatching – left half of front **ansi31**, angle 90, spacing 8. Brick parts of wall **brick** angle 0, spacing 1. Roof tiles **ar_rshke** angle 0, spacing 0.4 – Fig. 10.17.
6. Make layer **0** current and turn layer **HATCH** off.

Fig. 10.15 The completed
Front view

Fig. 10.16 The outline of the
hatched areas on layer
HATCH

Fig. 10.17 Hatching applied on
layer **HATCH01**

Questions

1. What is the abbreviation for the tool **Hatch**?
2. There are two methods of setting the parameters for hatching. What are they?
3. What is meant by *leaking* in reference to hatching and area of a drawing?
4. What needs to be changed if when a hatch pattern is applied to an area, there are gaps in the hatch pattern?
5. Two methods of ensuring that areas to be hatched in a drawing are correctly covered with the hatch pattern have been given. What are the two methods?
6. Some parts of a sectional view in engineering drawings should not be hatched. What are these parts?
7. How are those parts which should not be hatched in a sectional view in an engineering drawing shown in the section?
8. When two areas side by side showing different parts of an item in a section are to be hatched, how should you distinguish between the two parts?
9. What is a *part section*?
10. What is a *half section*?

Exercises

1. Fig. 10.18. Using the tools **PLINE** and **HATCH** copy the given pattern. Sizes are left to your own judgement.

Fig. 10.18 Exercise 1

2. Fig. 10.19. Using the tools **PLINE** and **HATCH** copy the given pattern. Sizes are left to your own judgement.

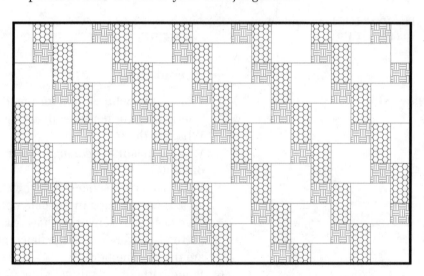

Fig. 10.19 Exercise 2

3. Fig. 10.20 is a photograph of a component from a machine and Fig. 10.21 a two-view Third angle orthographic projection of the component. Copy the two views to the given dimensions and add a sectional End view on the right of the given Front view, the section plane to pass through the centre line of the Front view. Add all necessary dimensions and include a title block, in which the component is named as **PART 73_A/4**.

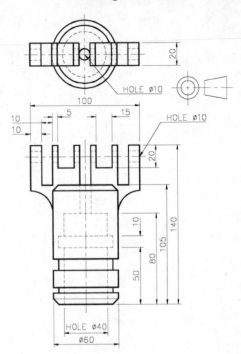

Fig. 10.21 Exercise 3

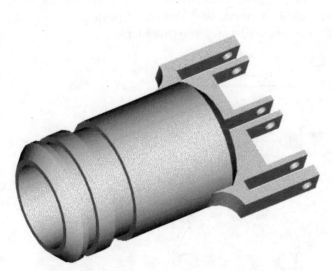

Fig. 10.20 A photograph of the component for Exercise 3

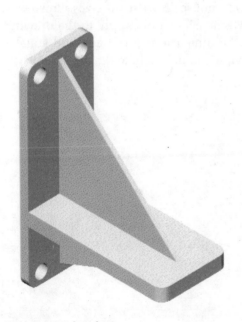

Fig. 10.22 A bracket

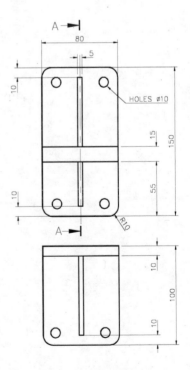

Fig. 10.23 Exercise 4

4. Fig. 10.23 is a Front view and Plan of the bracket shown in the photograph Fig. 10.22. Copy the two given views and add a sectional view on A-A. Add all necessary dimensions and a suitable title block.

5. Fig. 10.24. Copy the two given orthographic views and add a sectional view on A-A. Work in Third angle projection, add all necessary dimensions and a suitable title block.

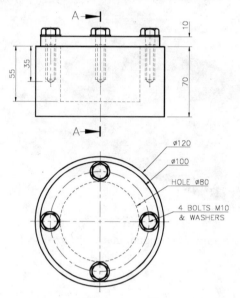

Fig 10.24 Exercise 5

6. Fig. 10.25 is a Front view of a house drawn to the sizes shown with the view. Obviously the dimensions only apply to the drawing. Copy the given view to the dimensions given and add suitable hatching patterns to the view. Do not include the dimensions.

Fig. 10.25 Exercise 6

CHAPTER 11

Pictorial drawing

Introduction

AutoCAD LT can be used for the construction of pictorial drawings such as isometric, cabinet and planometric, but does not have the facility to construct true perspective pictorial drawings. Simple one-point and two-point perspective drawings can be constructed, but these must not be confused with the truly perspective types of drawings which can be constructed in AutoCAD. Neither must it be assumed that the types of pictorial drawing which can be produced in AutoCAD LT are three-dimensional (3D) drawings. They are in fact two-dimensional (2D). 3D drawing facilities in AutoCAD LT are strictly limited. If true 3D drawings are required, then AutoCAD must be used.

Isometric drawing

In isometric drawing a pictorial view is built up on three axes – a vertical axis and two axes lying at 30° from the horizontal each side of the vertical axis. The graphics screen can be quickly set up for drawing on these isometric axes by either of the following methods:

1. Setting the check boxes **Isometric Snap/Grid**, **Snap** and **Grid** in the **Drawing Aids** dialogue box to show crosses (i.e. set them on), followed by a *left-click* on the **OK** button of the dialogue box (Fig. 11.1).
2. **Command:** *enter* snap *right-click*
    Snap spacing or ON/OFF/Rotate/Style <5>: *enter* s (Style) *right-click*
    Standard/Isometric <S>: *enter* i (Isometric) *right-click*
    Vertical spacing <5>: *right-click* (to accept the 5)
    Command:

No matter which of these two methods is used, the AutoCAD LT graphics window changes as shown in Fig. 11.2. An isometric drawing has a top, a left-hand side and a right-hand side.

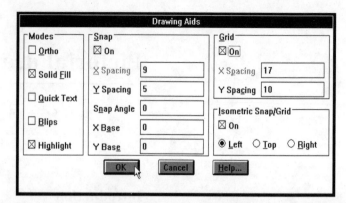

Fig. 11.1 Setting **Isometric Snap/Grid** in the **Drawing Aids** dialogue box

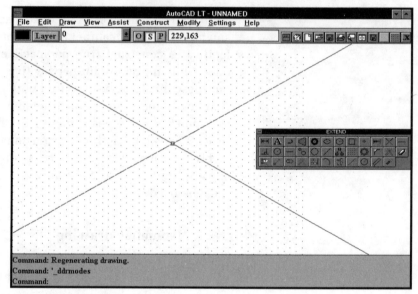

Fig. 11.2 The AutoCAD LT graphics window set up for isometric drawing

Isoplanes

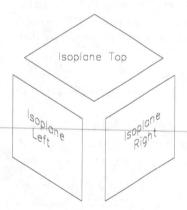

Fig. 11.3 The three Isoplanes

In AutoCAD LT these are known as **Isoplanes** – Fig. 11.3. The cursor lines in Fig. 11.2 show the **Isoplane** set to **Top**. Isoplanes can be set in the **Drawing Aids** dialogue box – by a *left-click* on any one of the three check circles marked **Left**, **Top** and **Right** in the **Isometric Grid/Snap** area of the dialogue box. In practice an easier method of setting the required isoplane is to press the two keyboard keys **Ctrl** and **E**. These toggle between the three isoplanes in the order **Top**, **Right** and **Left**. As the keys are repeatedly pressed the following appears at the command line:

Command: <Isoplane Top> <Isoplane Right> <Isoplane Left> informing the operator as to which isoplane is currently in use. As the construction of an isometric drawing continues, so the operator will need to be changing the positions of the isoplane cursor lines.

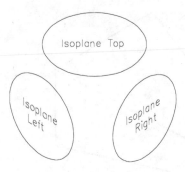

Fig. 11.4 Isometric ellipses

This is most easily carried out with the aid of the **Crl/E** keyboard short-cut. Using this combination of key strokes is much quicker than having to repeatedly call down the **Drawing Aids** dialogue box in order to change the isoplanes from the check circles in the **Isometric Grid/Snap** area of the dialogue box.

Using ORTHO in isometric drawing

The reader will soon find that if **Ortho** is on occasion set on (pressing key **F8** toggles **Ortho**) construction of an isometric drawing may be easier. The **Ortho** setting is along the axes, depending upon which **isoplane** is active. **Ortho** allows easier determination of the end points of lines in drawing based completely on the axes.

Isometric ellipses

Isometric ellipses are drawn by either selecting **Ellipse** from the **Draw** pull-down menu, or by *entering* el at the command line. In either case, the command line changes to:

> **Command:** *enter* el (for Ellipse) *right-click*
> **<Axis endpoint 1>/Center/Isocircle:** *enter* i (for Isocircle) *right-click*
> **<Circle radius>/Diameter:** *pick* a point on screen or *enter* coordinates
> **Command:**

and the ellipse for the isometric circle appears, the position of its axes dependent upon which Isoplane is in operation. In fact the Isoplane can be changed while the isocircle is being constructed if it appears that the wrong Isoplane is current (**Ctrl/E**).

Constructing isometric drawings

It is important to remember while constructing along isometric axes that true sizes can only be measured along either the vertical or the 30° axes. This is of particular importance if the edges of the item being drawn do not lie along the isometric axes. Fig. 11.5 shows this. Failure to observe this rule will result in a drawing that appears distorted.

Using absolute coordinates

Instead of using the isometric **Snap** and **Grid** points, an isometric drawing can be constructed with the aid of the absolute coordinate method of drawing. In some circumstances the operator may find this method to be of value. As an example the cube shown in

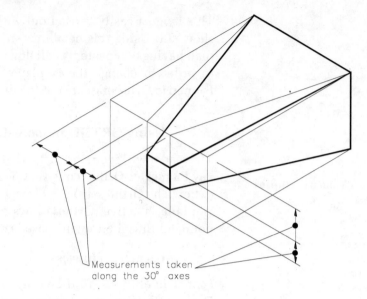

Fig. 11.5 Measurements must be taken along the isometric axes

Measurements taken along the 30° axes

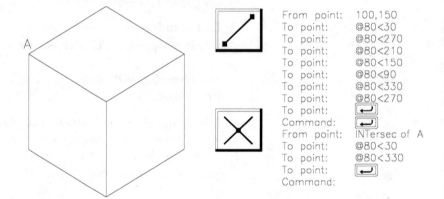

Fig. 11.6 An example of an isometric drawing of a cube constructed using absolute coordinates

```
From point:   100,150
To  point:    @80<30
To  point:    @80<270
To  point:    @80<210
To  point:    @80<150
To  point:    @80<90
To  point:    @80<330
To  point:    @80<270
To  point:    ⏎
Command:      ⏎
From point:   INTersec of A
To  point:    @80<30
To  point:    @80<330
To  point:    ⏎
Command:
```

Fig. 11.6 was constructed using absolute coordinates entered at the keyboard. Fig. 11.6 includes the tool icons and the sequence of absolute coordinates for constructing the cube. This method is normally not as easy to use as using the isometric grid produced with isometric snap and grid points. The reader is advised to copy this cube with the sequence of keyboard entries included with the drawing.

Examples of isometric drawings

Figures 11.7 to 11.10 are examples of isometric drawings. Try constructing these examples, without bothering too much about sizes. These examples show the following features:

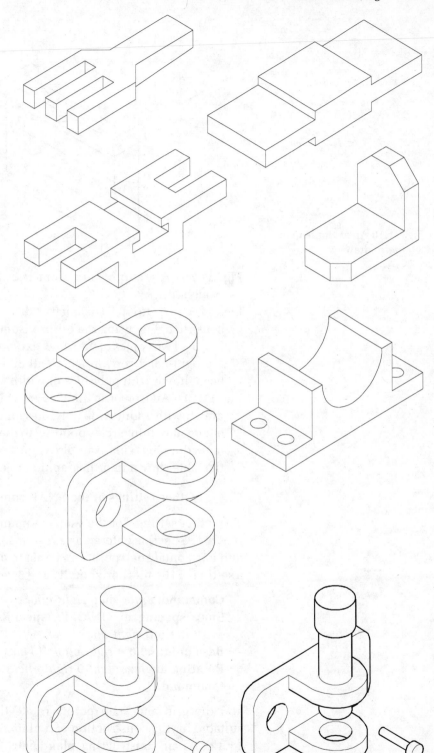

Fig. 11.7 Examples of isometric drawing

Fig. 11.8 Examples of isometric drawing

Fig. 11.9 Examples of exploded isometric drawings

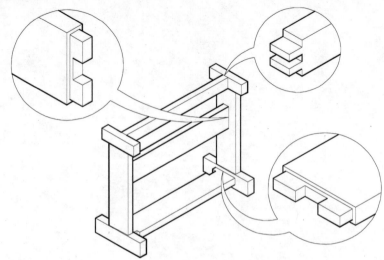

Fig. 11.10 An example of an isometric drawing

Fig. 11.7 – A group of four isometric drawings all made up from straight lines.

Fig. 11.8 – A group of isometric drawings which include curves constructed by using the **Ellipse/Isometric circle** tool.

Fig. 11.9 – Two copies of the same 'exploded' isometric drawing, with the right-hand copy in which all outer lines of the drawing have been drawn with polylines of width 1 unit.

Fig. 11.10 – An isometric drawing in which all outer lines have been drawn with 1 unit wide polylines and in which details have been enlarged within circles pointing to the position of the detail in the main drawing. This example is a pictorial drawing of main body of the table shown in orthographic projection in Fig. 9.7.

Other settings of the SNAP command

Two other settings for the snap command are **Aspect** and **Rotation**. If a (for Aspect) is entered as a response, the settings of the vertical and horizontal snap point can be set to different sizes – for example a setting of 10 units horizontally and 5 vertically. Respond with an r:

Command: *enter* snap *right-click*
Snap spacing or ON/OFF/Aspect/Rotation/Style <5>: *enter* r (Rotation) *right-click*
Base point <0,0>: *right-click* (to accept 0,0)
Rotation angle: *enter* 30 *right-click*
Command:

and the grid and snap points rotate through 30° – Fig. 11.11 – suitable for the construction of a planometric drawing such as Fig. 11.12. When constructing planometric drawing the axes can be either 90°, 60°, 30° or 90°, 45°,45°. This type of drawing is of value

Fig. 11.11 The AutoCAD LT
window with snap (and grid)
rotation set to 30°

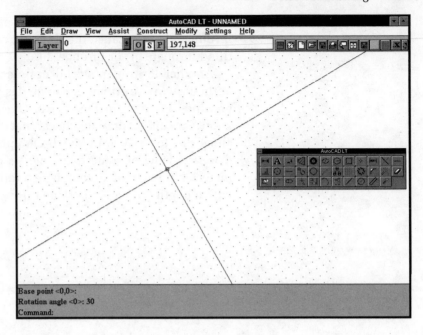

Fig. 11.12 An example of a
planometric drawing

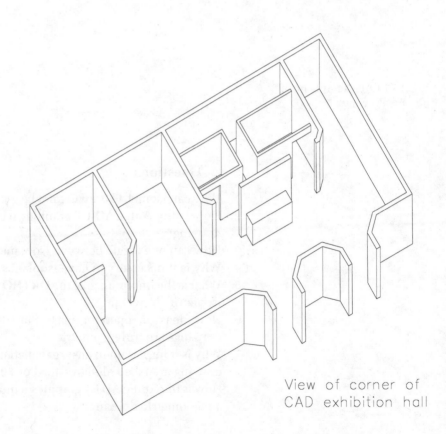

View of corner of
CAD exhibition hall

when attempting a pictorial drawing of an architectural or building layout. This is because the drawing can be based on a plan view tilted through 45° or through 30°.

Another form of pictorial drawing which can be constructed without snap and grid points rotated is *oblique* drawing, an example of which is given in Fig. 11.13. One type of oblique drawing is known as *cabinet* drawing. In cabinet drawing all dimensions taken along the 45° axis are halved. Oblique drawing can give a rather distorted view of some items, but is of value when attempting a pictorial drawing of an item with a rather complicated outline, but with a depth which is the same throughout.

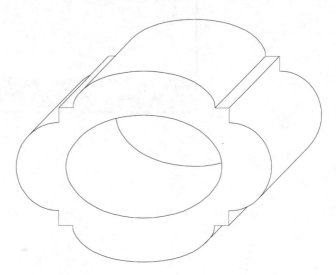

Fig. 11.13 An example of an oblique drawing

Questions

1. Why can isometric drawing not be regarded as true 3D drawing?
2. How is the AutoCAD LT graphics window set up for isometric drawing?
3. How can one toggle between isoplanes?
4. Why is it necessary to have isoplanes in AutoCAD LT?
5. What is the importance of the **ORTHO** tool when constructing an isometric drawing?
6. How does an operator make sure that ellipses in isometric drawings are truly isometric?
7. Why is it important to ensure that all measurements in isometric drawing are taken along vertical or 30° axes?
8. How is the AutoCAD LT graphics window set up for constructing a planometric drawing?

9. What is the purpose of the **Aspect** prompt in the **Snap** command sequence?

10. If you wished to construct an oblique pictorial drawing how could the **Snap** settings be set up?

Exercises

1. Construct a full size isometric drawing of the item shown in Fig. 11.14.

2. Construct a full size isometric drawing of the item shown in Fig. 11.15.

3. Working to the given dimensions construct a planometric drawing of the walls and floor shown in Fig. 11.16.

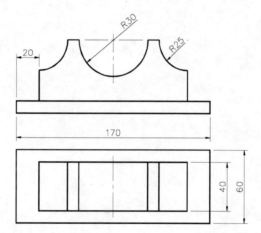

Fig. 11.14 Exercise 1

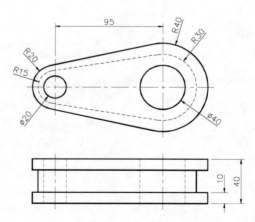

Fig. 11.15 Exercise 2

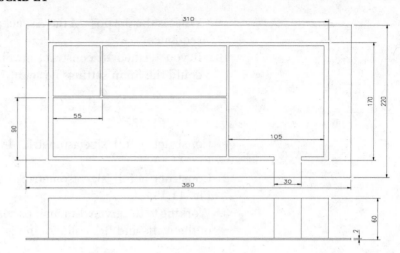

Fig. 11.16 Exercise 3

CHAPTER 12

Other Assist and Modify commands

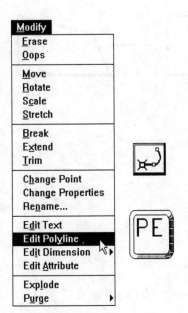

Fig. 12.1 Calling **Pedit**

Introduction

This chapter deals with some of the commands (tools) in the **Assist** and **Modify** menus, which have not as yet been described in earlier chapters and to give further details about some of the tools from these two menus which have already been partly dealt with.

Polylines

Polylines (plines) can be either a single segment or made up of a number of segments (Fig. 12.2). The segments may be either straight plines or plines formed from curves. Polylines may be open or closed. When acted upon by tools such as **Move**, **Copy** or **Mirror** all segments in a polyline are affected whether it is open or closed.

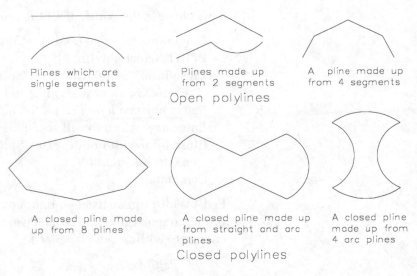

Fig. 12.2 Some examples of **Polylines**

Edit Polyline

The **Edit Polyline** tool is for editing plines. Its other name is **Pedit**. When the tool is selected the command line shows:

Command: *enter* pe (Pedit) *right-click*
PEDIT Select polyline:
**Close/Join/Width/Edit vertex/Spline/Decurve/Ltype gen/Undo/
eXit/<X>:**

Fig. 12.3 shows the results of responses to some of the prompts of **Pedit**.

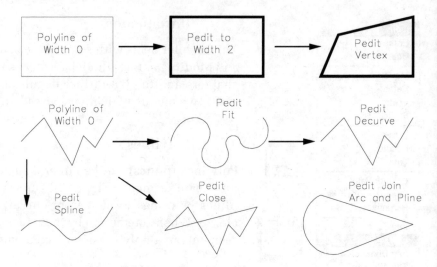

Fig. 12.3 The results of responses to some of the **Pedit** prompts

Pedit Width

This changes the width of all the segments in a pline.

Command: *enter* pe (Pedit) *right-click*
PEDIT Select polyline:
**Close/Join/Width/Edit vertex/Spline/Decurve/Ltype gen/Undo/
eXit/<X>:** *enter* w (Width) *right-click*
Select objects: *left-click* on the polyline
Enter new width for all segments: *enter* 2 (say) *right-click*
**Close/Join/Width/Edit vertex/Spline/Decurve/Ltype gen/Undo/
eXit/<X>:** *right-click*
Command:

Pedit Width can be used on lines constructed with the **Line** tool. A prompt requests the line be changed to a pline and from then on the change to a pline can take place.

Pedit vertex

If the response to the initial set of prompts is e (Edit vertex), a cross appears at the first vertex of the pline – the point at which a start was made in drawing the pline. The required vertex is chosen by repeated *right-clicks* which cause the cross to move to the next vertex in the direction in which the pline was drawn in response to the default **<N>** prompt. As an example of editing a vertex, using the **Move** prompt, the command line shows:

Command: *enter* pe (Pedit) *right-click*
PEDIT Select polyline:
Close/Join/Width/Edit vertex/Spline/Decurve/Ltype gen/Undo/
 eXit/<X>: *enter* e (Edit vertex) *right-click*
Next/Previous/Break/Insert/Move/Regen/Straighten/Tangent/Width/
 eXit<N>: *enter* m (Move) *right-click*
Enter new location: *left-click* at new point
Next/Previous/Break/Insert/Move/Regen/Straighten/Tangent/Width/
 eXit<N>: *enter* x (eXit) *right-click*
Close/Join/Width/Edit vertex/Spline/Decurve/Ltype gen/Undo/
 eXit/<X>: *right-click*
Command:

Other Edit vertex responses are not described here, but the reader is advised to attempt each in turn to see the resulting effects.

Pedit Fit

This allows a pline consisting of straight line segments to be fitted to a curve passing through all the vertices.

Command: *enter* pe (Pedit) *right-click*
PEDIT Select polyline: *left-click* on pline
Close/Join/Width/Edit vertex/Spline/Decurve/Ltype gen/Undo/
 eXit/<X>: *enter* f (Fit) *right-click*
Close/Join/Width/Edit vertex/Spline/Decurve/Ltype gen/Undo/
 eXit/<X>: *right-click*
Command:

Two examples are given. In Fig. 12.3 a pline made from straight segments is changed to a curve. In Fig. 12.4 a parabolic curve has

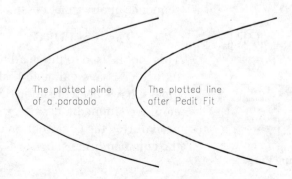

The plotted pline of a parabola

The plotted line after Pedit Fit

Fig. 12.4 A parabolic curve formed with the aid of **Pedit Fit**

been plotted and a pline drawn joining the plot points. This pline, consisting as it does of a series of straight lines, is changed to a true parabolic curve with the aid of **Pedit Fit**.

Pedit Close

Command: *enter* pe (Pedit) *right-click*
PEDIT Select polyline:
**Close/Join/Width/Edit vertex/Spline/Decurve/Ltype gen/Undo/
eXit/<X>:** *enter* c (Close) *right-click*
**Close/Join/Width/Edit vertex/Spline/Decurve/Ltype gen/Undo/
eXit/<X>:** *right-click*
Command:

and an open pline will close with either a straight pline joining the open ends, or with a curve if the pline being closed contains curves at its ends.

Pedit Join

Command: *enter* pe (Pedit) *right-click*
PEDIT Select polyline:
**Close/Join/Width/Edit vertex/Spline/Decurve/Ltype gen/Undo/
eXit/<X>:** *enter* j (Join) *right-click*
Select objects: *left-click* on the entity **1 found**
Select objects: *left-click* on the entity **1 found**
Select objects: *right-click*
Command:

and plines made up from unconnected segments will join to form a single pline. Lines and/or arcs can be joined to polylines using this prompt. The arcs and/or lines are changed to plines in the joining process.

Pedit Decurve, Undo and eXit

Errors when using **Pedit** can be undone by *entering* u (Undo). The last **Pedit** operation is undone. **Decurve** changes all curves into straight pline. When one wishes to get out of the **Pedit** command sequence at any time, *enter* x (for eXit) and the sequence ends.

The tool PURGE

This tool is used to purge all unwanted data from any drawing file. Its use can save valuable disk space, particularly if a number of blocks have been inserted in a drawing. The tool can only be employed immediately after a drawing has been loaded. It cannot be used during the construction of a drawing. When the tool is called, the command line shows:

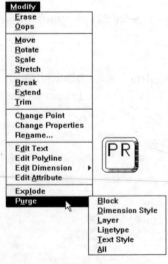

Fig. 12.5 Calling **Purge**

Command: *enter* pr *right-click*
Purge unused Blocks/Dimstyles/LAyers/LTypes/SHapes/STyles/
  All: *enter* a (All) *right-click*
Purge Block Fig04? <N>: *enter* y (Yes) *right-click*

followed by a series of prompts suggesting all unnecessary features in the drawing which can be purged.

Tools from the Assist menu

In this chapter we will deal with only the last set of tools in the **Assist** pull-down menu. Other features from this menu will be dealt with later in this book.

The tool DISTANCE

For finding the distance between any two selected points in the AutoCAD LT graphics window.

Command: *enter* di *right-click*
DIST Firstpoint: *pick* **Second point**: *pick*
**Distance = 259, Angle in XY Plane = 326, Angle from XY plane
  = 0**
Delta X = 215, Delta Y = -145, Delta Z = 0
Command:

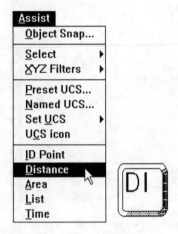

Fig. 12.6 Calling **Distance**

showing information about the distance, angles in and from the plane of the graphics window and the X and Y distances between the two points.

The tool AREA

This tool allows the operator to find the area enclosed within selected points on the screen.

Command: *enter* aa *right-click*
<First point>/Entity/Add/Subtract:
Next point:
Next point:
Next point:
Area = 100000 Perimeter = 400
Command:

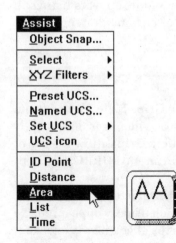

Fig. 12.7 Calling **Area**

The above shows the area enclosed in a square of 100 units side length. The area is in units^2, the length of the perimeter is in units.

If the area of an **Entity** such as a circle, ellipse or closed polyline is required, use the e response. If areas are to be added or subtracted use the s response.

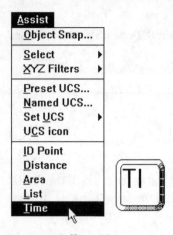

Fig. 12.8 Calling **Time**

The tool TIME

When the **Time** tool is called an AutoCAD LT text window appears listing all the times involved in the drawing currently under construction. Fig. 12.8 shows the methods of calling the tool and Fig. 12.9 a typical text window resulting from the action of the tool. No prompts appear at the command line.

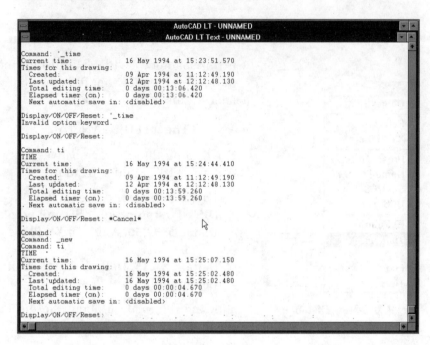

Fig. 12.9 A typical AutoCAD LT text window giving the times involved in the current drawing in the graphics window

The tool LIST

Call **List** and another AutoCAD LT text window appears listing all the details about the entities within the current drawing in the graphics window.

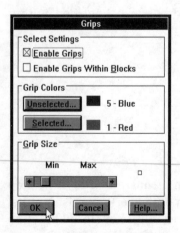

Fig. 12.10 Setting **Grips** in the **Grips** dialogue box

Grips

If the **Enable Grips** check box is set in the **Grips** dialogue box (from **Settings**) – Fig. 12.10 – grip boxes appear whenever an entity is selected without a command being in action. **Grips** allow the use of the tools **STRETCH**, **MOVE**, **ROTATE**, **SCALE** and **MIRROR** without having to call them in any way.

There are two types of **Grip** boxes – **Unselected** which usually appears in a blue colour and **Selected** which usually appear red. To use **Grips**, first make sure the **Enable Grips** check box is checked, then *left-click* on the entity to be modified. Blue grip boxes appear around the entity, which also highlights (Fig. 12.11). *Left-click* on the grip box to be used as a base point. It becomes a **Selected** box and turns red. The command line changes to:

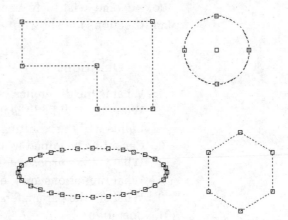

Fig. 12.11 Grips as they appear in the graphic window

    STRETCH

with a corresponding series of stretch prompts. A *right-click* and the command line changes to:

    MOVE

with another series of move prompts. *Right-click* again.

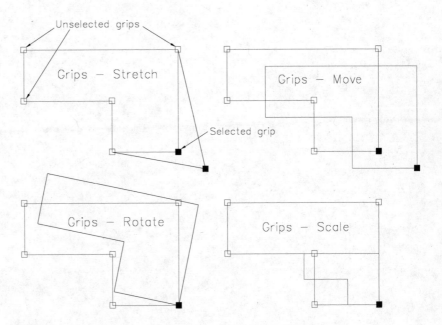

Fig. 12.12 The effects of using **Grips** commands

ROTATE

appears with its set of prompts. This continues with ****SCALE****
and ****MIRROR****. The operator decides which of these modify
tools he/she wishes to use. The results of some of these **Grips**
modifications are shown in Fig. 12.12.

Questions

1. What is the difference between a closed and an open polyline?
2. When the tool Pedit is used with its Fit prompt, through which
   points will the resulting curve pass?
3. Can a line be joined to a pline? If so, how?
4. What is the purpose of the tool **Purge**?
5. What limitations are there on the **Purge** tool?
6. What are the parameters displayed when the **Distance** tool is in
   operation?
7. In which units are the figures displayed at the command line in
   response to the **Area** tool?
8. What is the purpose of using the tool **Time** in AutoCAD LT?
9. Can you name the modify tools which can be operated with the
   use of **Grips**?
10. What is an AutoCAD LT Text window?

CHAPTER 13

3D facilities in AutoCAD LT

Introduction

AutoCAD LT includes a limited 3D facility, which allows the loading of 3D solid model drawings created in AutoCAD or in the Advanced Modelling Extension (AME), together with limited editing of the loaded 3D models. In order to facilitate the loading and part editing of 3D models, the coordinate system of AutoCAD LT includes a third axis – the Z axis – with an imaginary direction positively outwards perpendicularly from the graphics window. Fig. 13.1 illustrates the positive and negative directions of the three coordinate axes.

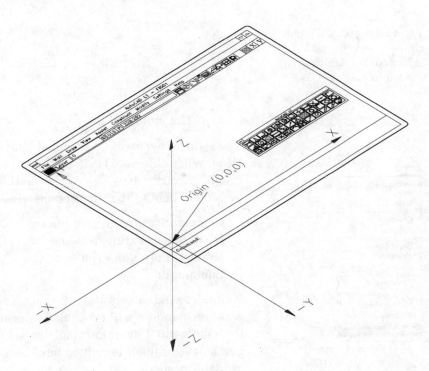

Fig. 13.1 The X,Y,Z coordinate axes of AutoCAD LT

An example of a solid model drawing

Fig. 13.2 is an AutoVision rendering of the AME solid model drawing shown in Fig. 13.3. This solid model will be used to show some of the 3D capabilities of AutoCAD LT. To start with it can be loaded as a drawing into AutoCAD LT. It can then be acted upon by the following tools (commands):

Fig. 13.2 An AutoVision rendering of a solid model to be loaded into AutoCAD LT

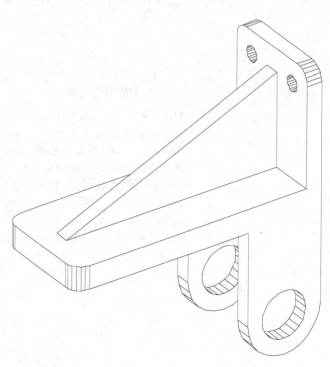

Fig. 13.3 A 3D solid model drawing constructed in AutoCAD for Windows and loaded into AutoCAD LT

The tool HIDE

The solid shown in Fig. 13.3 has already been acted upon by the tool **Hide**. When the tool is called all that is required is for the operator to *left-click* on the drawing on screen and hidden lines will automatically be hidden behind the surfaces showing to the front.

> **Command:** *enter* hi *right-click*
> **HIDE Regenerating drawing**
> **Hidden lines: done 100%**
> **Command:**

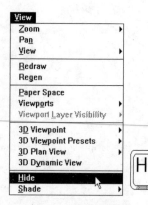

Fig. 13. 4 Calling **Hide**

If the drawing is complex, the removal of hidden lines from the graphics window will take some time and messages will appear at the command line informing the operator of the progress as a percentage of the lines which have been hidden. To bring back the hidden lines:

Fig. 13.5 Calling **Shade**

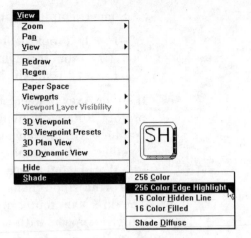

Command: *enter* rg (for Regen) *right-click*

The tool SHADE

A very limited form of rendering is available in AutoCAD LT with the aid of the **Shade** tool. The shaded solid model Fig. 13.6 was the result of using the **256 Color Edge Highlight** option. The command line shows:

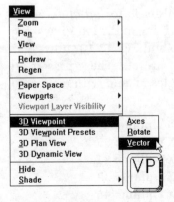

Command: *enter* sh *right-click*
SHADE Regenerating drawing.
Shading in 17 passes.
Shading complete.
Command:

Fig. 13.6 The results of using **Shade** with the **256 Color Edge Highlight** option

The reader is advised to attempt using the tool applying the other options showing in the **Shade** sub-menu from the **View** pull-down menu.

VPOINT

Vpoint allows a 3D drawing to be viewed from any direction in the *x,y,z* coordinate area. When the command is called:

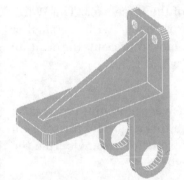

Command: *enter* vp *right-click*
VPOINT Rotate/<Viewpoint>:<0,0,1>:

The figures **<0,0,1>** indicate the position from which the 3D drawing is currently viewed. The coordinate figures represent only the direction of the viewing point, not the distance of the viewing point from the 3D model. Thus the **<0,0,1>** indicates that the viewing point is +Z from the model – i.e. from above. In other words the view as seen is a plan view.

Fig. 13.7 Calling **Vpoint**

Some examples of other viewing points would be:

–1,–1,1   From the left (–X), from the front (–Y) and above (+Z)
1,1,1   From the right (+X), from behind (+Y) and above (+Z)
–1,–1,–1   From the left (–X), from the front (–Y) and below (–Z)

If either **Axes** is selected from the **3D Viewpoint** sub-menu, or the prompt **Rotate/<Viewpoint>:** is answered with a *right-click*, the graphics window changes and a tripod marked with X, Y and Z together with a double circle with a small cross within its outline (the World icon) appear – Fig. 13.8. As the mouse is moved, so the axes of the tripod change and the cross within the World icon moves. The three axes represent the directions of the axes of the 3D model which reappears with a *right-click* in the window once the axes have been determined under mouse control. The model position is now seen to be based upon the directions of the three axes. The World icon represents a view of the world from above with the smaller circle representing the equator. The tiny cross represents the position of the viewing point in relation to the world plan.

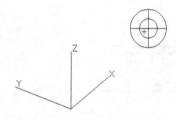

Fig. 13.8 The axes and World icon appearing with a *right-click* to the **Vpoint** prompt

VPOINT Rotate

Another way of setting the axes is to answer the **Vpoint** prompts by *entering* an r (for Rotate), followed by setting angles for the rotation of the 3D model in both the XY plane itself and the angle from the XY plane. The command line changes to:

Enter angle in XY plane: *enter* 30 (say) *right-click*
Enter angle from XY plane: *enter* 30 (say) *right-click*
Command:

The 3D model then assumes a position which is 30° in the XY plane and 30° from the XY plane.

3D Viewpoint Presets

Yet another way of setting viewing points is to *left-click* on **3D Viewpoint Presets**, followed by selecting one of the **Iso Views**. Fig. 13.9 shows the choices in the sub-menu and Fig. 13.10 shows a 3D model in each of the four 3D viewpoint presets. These presets are equivalent to the following Rotation angles in, and with respect to, the XY plane:

Fig. 13.9 The sub-menu for **3D Viewpoint Presets** from the **View** pull-down menu

Viewpoint Iso SW: or   **angle in XY plane:** 225
                                angle to XY plane: 35
Viewpoint Iso SE: or   **angle in XY plane:** 315
                                angle to XY plane: 35
Viewpoint Iso NE: or   **angle in XY plane:** 45
                                angle to XY plane: 35

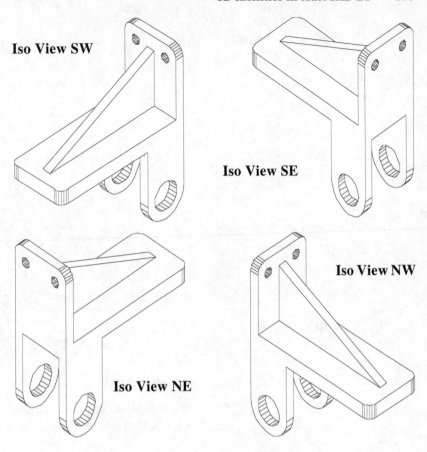

Iso View SW

Iso View SE

Iso View NW

Iso View NE

Fig. 13.10 Four views using
the **3D Viewpoint Presets** from
the **View** pull-down menu

Viewpoint Iso NW: or   **angle in XY plane:** 135
angle to XY plane: 35

Fig. 13.10 shows the four **Viewpoint ISO** views. Each of the views
in this illustration have been acted upon by **HIDE**.

In addition the viewpoints can be set to show a 3D model from the
Top, **Front**, **Left**, **Right** or **Back** by selection from the sub-menu of the
3D Viewpoint Presets. See Fig. 13.9. Fig. 13.11 illustrates these
views.

The User Coordinate System (UCS)

When setting the viewing position for viewing a 3D model with
Vpoint, the 3D model with the XY plane is moved. When viewing a
3D model in the **User Coordinate System (UCS)** the XY plane moves,
with the model. In effect the results are similar. The UCS allows the
operator to place the XY plane at any angle or slope.

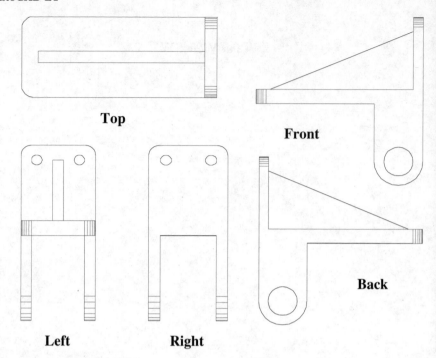

Top

Front

Back

Fig. 13.11 More **3D Viewpoint Presets**

Left   **Right**

UCSFOLLOW

Before the XY plane can be changed with the aid of the UCS, the variable **UCSFOLLOW** must first be set to 1, as follows:

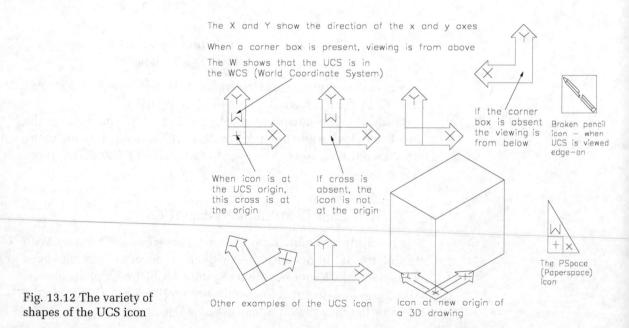

The X and Y show the direction of the x and y axes

When a corner box is present, viewing is from above

The W shows that the UCS is in the WCS (World Coordinate System)

If the corner box is absent the viewing is from below

Broken pencil icon — when UCS is viewed edge—on

When icon is at the UCS origin, this cross is at the origin

If cross is absent, the icon is not at the origin

The PSpace (Paperspace) icon

Fig. 13.12 The variety of shapes of the UCS icon

Other examples of the UCS icon

Icon at new origin of a 3D drawing

Command: *enter* ucsfollow *right-click*
New value for UCSFOLLOW<0>: *enter* 1 *right-click*
Command:

The UCS icon

It is also advisable to have the UCS icon showing at the bottom right hand corner of the Graphics window. If the UCS icon is not already showing there:

Command: *enter* ucs icon *right-click*
ON/OFF/All/Noorigin/ORigin <OFF>: *enter* ON *right-click*
Command:

The icon can take a variety of forms as illustrated in Fig. 13.12. The UCS can be set using a number of methods. To set the UCS at orthogonal angles - at right angles to each other - *left-click* on **Assist** in the menu bar, followed by a *left-click* on **UCS Presets...** in the pull-down menu. The **UCS Orientation** dialogue box appears. - Fig. 13.13.

Fig. 13.13 The **UCS Orientation** dialogue box

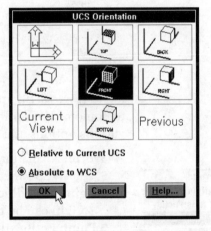

Fig. 13.14 shows a 3D model as it would appear in several of the **UCS** orientations from the dialogue box - **Top**, **Bottom**, **Left** and **Right**. A *left-click* in the relevant box of the dialogue box, followed by another *left-click on* the **OK** button, and the model changes to its new UCS orientation. Make sure the **Absolute to WCS** (World Coordinate System) is checked. The **WCS** is the original XY plane as it appears when AutoCAD LT is first opened.

Other settings of the UCS

Fig. 13.14 An AutoVision rendering of the 3D model for Fig. 13.15

Left-click on **Assist** in the menu bar, followed by another *left-click* on **Set UCS** in the pull-down menu which appears. The **Set UCS** sub-

Fig. 13.15 Four **UCS**
Orientation presets

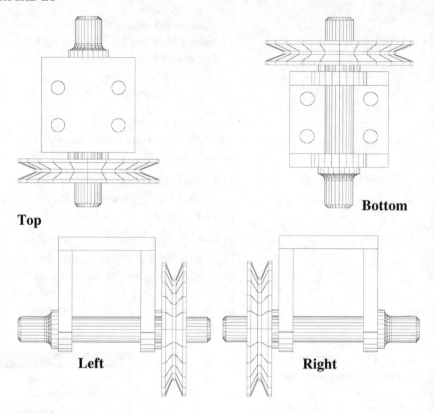

Top

Bottom

Left

Right

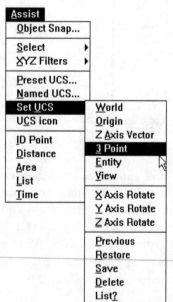

Fig. 13.16 **Set UCS** sub-menu
from the **Assist** pull-down
menu

menu (Fig. 13.16) appears. Fig. 13.17 shows the results of working to some of the options within this sub-menu. The actions of the various options are:

World: No matter in which UCS the model is placed, it reverts to the **WCS** - the original AutoCAD LT XY plane (Fig. 13.17).

Origin: Providing the **UCSICON** setting is **OR** (Origin), a new origin can be picked on a 3D model (Fig. 13.17).

3 Point: Follow the prompts which appear at the command line when this selection is made. The **3 Point** view shown in Fig. 13.17 has resulted in a front view of the model.

Entity: *Left-click* on any entity in a 3D model and the model aligns its UCS to the entity.

View: Used in conjunction with **Previous**, **Restore**, **Save**, **Delete**, and **List?**. A saved view can be restored, deleted or listed. The list appears in an AutoCAD LT text window.

X, **Y** and **Z Rotates:** Follow the prompts at the command line which request a rotation angle. These three prompts can be used one after the other to obtain a view as seen when the UCS is rotated around one, two or all three coordinate axes.

Fig. 13.17 Some **Set UCS**
settings

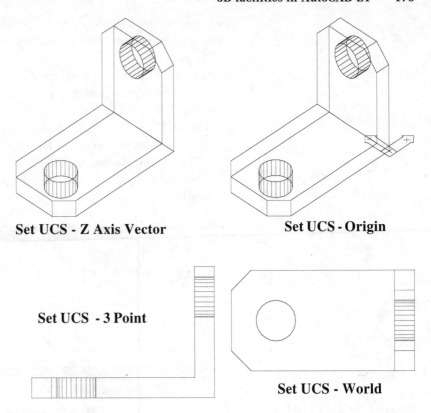

Set UCS - Z Axis Vector

Set UCS - Origin

Set UCS - 3 Point

Set UCS - World

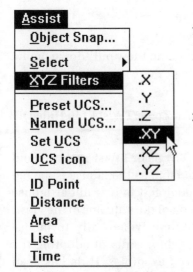

Fig. 13.18 The **XYZ Filters**
sub-menu

Notes

1. After using any of the **Set UCS** commands (tools) it may be necessary to **Zoom** back to 1 (scale at which the drawing was constructed). This is because after using any of these tools, the screen reverts to a **Zoom All** situation, which may not be convenient for the operator to continue work with the model.

2. It will be found that the **XYZ Filters** from the **Assist** menu (Fig. 13.18) may be required when setting a **3 Point** setting. As an example when **3 Point** is called, the command line shows:

Command: UCS
Origin/ZAxis/3point/Entity/View/X/Y/Z/Prev/Restore/Save/Del/?/
    <World>: _3point
Origin point<0,0,0>: *pick*
Positive point of X-axis: *pick*
Point on positive-Y portion of the UCS XY plane: *left-click* on
    .XY in the sub menu **.XY of** *pick* **(need Z):** *enter* 1 *right-click*
Command:

3. Note the **(need Z)** response is 1 (could be –1). This is because this Z coordinate figure only gives the direction along the Z axis and not the distance.

4. The **XYZ Filters** have other uses than that shown above. The reader will come across further uses of these filters when the occasion arises.

5. When a UCS is saved, it should be given a name. A named view which has been saved can be recalled by a *left-click* on **Named UCS...** in the **Assist** pull-down menu. This brings up the **UCS Control** dialogue box (Fig. 13.19) from which a saved UCS can be recalled.

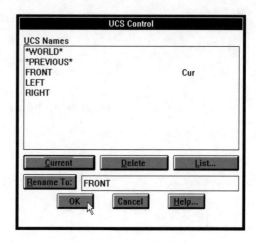

Fig. 13.19 The **UCS Control** dialogue box from which any saved UCS can be restored

3D Dynamic View

When **3D Dynamic view** is selected from the **View** pull-down menu, the command line shows the following:

Command: DVIEW
CAmera/TArget/Distance/POints/PAn/Zoom/TWist/CLip/Hide/Off/
   Undo/<eXit>:

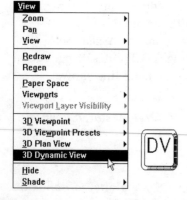

Fig. 13.20 Calling **3D Dynamic View**

When the response is either **CAmera**, **TArget** or **TWist** a rubber band line becomes attached to the 3D model and as the mouse is moved a ghosted model replaces the 3D model and moves under mouse control giving the operator an indication of the outcome of the view. In other words the model is responding dynamically to mouse movement. Fig. 13.21 shows some of the results of adopting the various responses. In each of the given examples, **Hide** has been called to hide all hidden lines. Note the perspective icon in the **Distance** view.

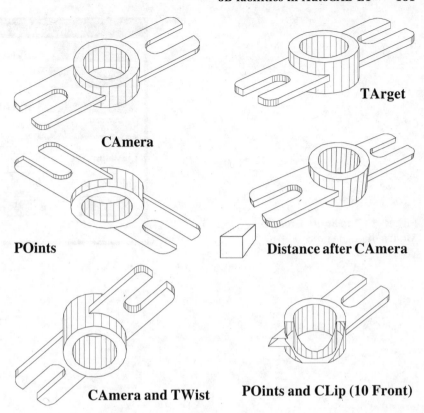

Fig. 13.21 Some Dynamic
Views

The tool ELEVATION

Left-click on the Layer colour button at the top left-hand corner of
the graphics window (Fig. 13.22). The **Entity Creation Modes** dialogue
box appears (Fig. 13.23). In the dialogue box *enter* 50 in the **Thickness**
box, followed by a *left-click* on the **OK** button of the dialogue box.
The dialogue box can also be called from the **Settings** pull-down
menu.

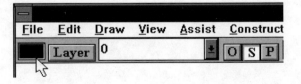

Fig. 13.22 Selecting the Layer
colour button

The settings for Elevation and Thickness can also be set from the
command line by *entering* ev (for elevation) at the command line:

Command: *enter* ev *right-click*
ELEV New current elevation<0>: *right-click* (accepts the 0)
New current thickness<0>: *enter* 50 *right-click*

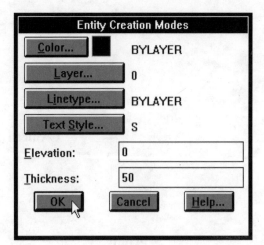

Fig. 13.23 The **Entity Creation Modes** dialogue box

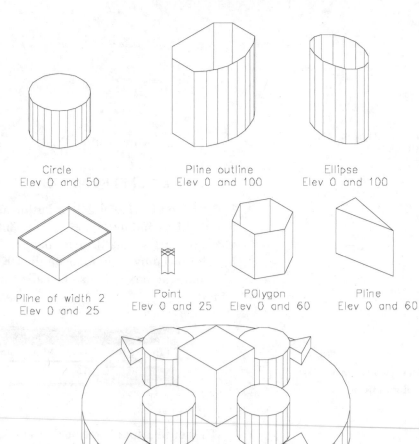

Fig. 13.24 Examples of entities with elevations

Fig. 13.25 A simple block built up on differing elevations

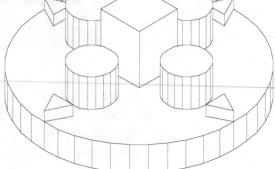

With the aid of these settings simple 3D models can be built up from entities drawn with the aid of the **Draw** tools. Examples are given in Fig. 13.24. An example of a simple block constructed on differing elevations is given in Fig. 13.25. The given examples have all been acted upon by **Hide**. Note that the circle and the plines have tops behind which lines are hidden, whereas the other examples are open at their upper faces. Note also that the plines, which in plan view would be solid filled lines are no longer solid filled when in an elevation situation.

Viewports

Left-click on **Viewports** in the **View** pull-down menu. The **Viewports** sub-menu appears (Fig. 13.26). A variety of different viewport layouts is available (Fig. 13.27). The selection of the particular

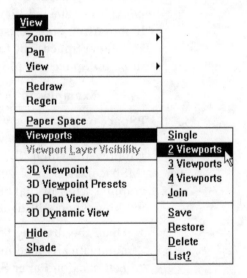

Fig. 13.26 The **Viewports** sub-menu from the **View** pull-down menu

viewport configuration desired is selected first with a *left-click* on **2**, **3** or **4 Viewports** in the **Viewports** sub-menu. The command line changes to:

> **Command: _vports**
> **Save/Restore/ | Delete/Join/Single/2/<3>/4: 3**
> **Horizontal/Vertical/Above/Below/Left:** *enter* h *right-click*

and the graphics window becomes divided into 3 viewports spaced as shown in the Horizontal configuration in Fig. 13.27. The current viewport in which construction could proceed is outlined in a thick line. The current viewport can be changed by moving the cursor

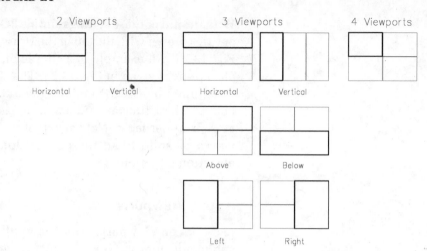

Fig. 13.27 The various viewport configurations

under mouse control into the required viewport, followed by a *left-click*. The selected viewport then becomes the current viewport. Before using viewports it is necessary to understand **Model Space** and **Paper Space**. The following seven examples of using viewports in both **PSpace** and **MSpace** should clarify their uses.

Examples in the use of viewports

PSpace only has uses with 3D models. There is not much point in using **PSpace** for 2D work. The normal AutoCAD LT graphics window in which 2D drawings are constructed is **Model Space** (MSpace). It is only when 3D models have been loaded into the graphics window that **PSpace** (Paper Space) is of value. The order of working when editing 3D models is:

1. Open the drawing file containing the 3D model data. This will automatically load into **MSpace**.
2. *Left-click* on **Paper Space** in the **View pull**-down menu. The 3D model in **MSpace** disappears from the window, which becomes blank, with a prompt at the command line:

   Entering Paper Space. Use MVIEW to insert Model Space viewports.
   Command:

3. Call **MVIEW** as follows:

   Command: *enter* mv (Mview) *right-click*
   ON/OFF/Hideplot/Fit/2/3/4/<First point>: *enter* 4 *right-click*
   Fit/<First point>: *enter* f (Fit) *right-click*
   Command:

   Fig. 13.29 shows the results of entering MVIEW in 4 viewports.

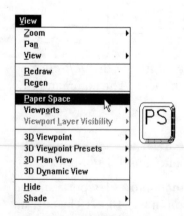

Fig. 13.28 Calling **Paper Space**

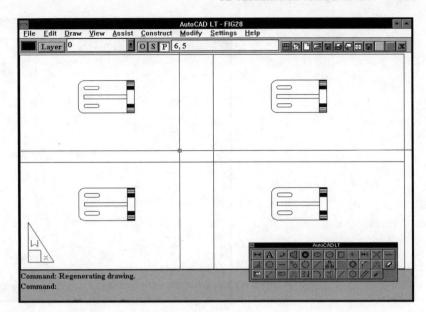

Fig. 13.29 Entering **MVIEW** with 4 viewports

4. Go back to **MSpace** (Model Space):

   Command: *enter* ms (MSpace) *right-click*
   MSPACE
   Command:

5. In each the four viewports turn **UCSFOLLOW** off by:

   Command: *enter* ucsfollow *right-click*
   New value for UCSFOLLOW<1>: *enter* 0 *right-click*
   Command:

6. In the viewports:

   Top left **VPOINT** set to **0,–1,0**
   Top right **VPOINT** set to **–1,0,0**
   Bottom left **VPOINT** set to **0,0,1**
   Bottom right **VPOINT** set to **–1,–1,1**
   In all viewports **HIDE**

   The results are shown in Fig. 13.30.

7. Now go back to **PSpace** by:

   Command: *enter* ps *right-click*

   The result is shown in Fig. 13.31.

While in **PSpace** the viewports containing the different views of the 3D model can be moved, mirrored, stretched or scaled. However it is the viewport on which the action of these tools takes place, the 3D

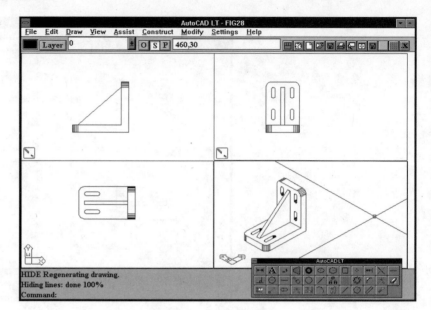

Fig. 13.30 The 3D model in **MSpace** after new viewpoints have been set

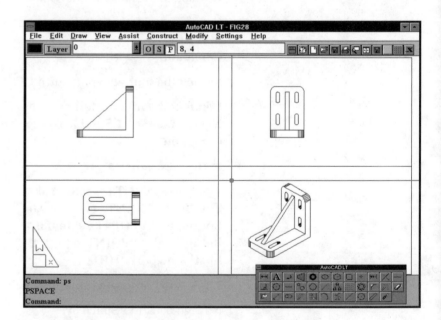

Fig. 13.31 Back into **PSpace** with the 3D model in the four viewports

model in the viewport being unchanged. To move a viewport, *left-click* on one of its edges and, holding the left button down, *drag* the viewport to its new position under mouse control. Fig. 13.32 shows the result.

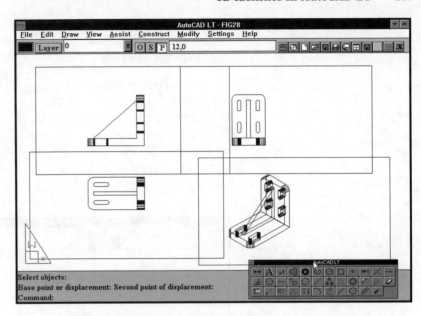

Fig. 13.32 Moving viewports in **PSpace**

Hiding the viewport edges

The edges of the viewports can be hidden by:

1. When in **PSpace** before calling **MVIEW** to determine the number of viewports, make a new layer named **VPORTS** preferably of a different colour to the entities making up the 3D model. Make the layer **VPORTS** current.
2. Call **MVIEW** and set the number of viewports. The 3D model appears in **PSpace**.

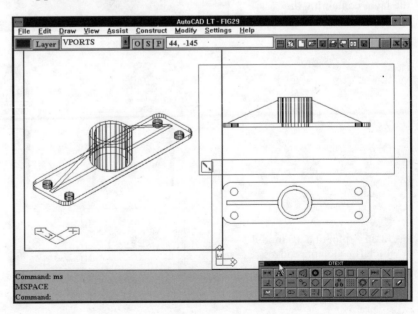

Fig. 13.33 A 3D model in a 3 viewport setting in **MSpace**

3. Turn layer **VPORTS** off. The edges of the viewports disappear from the graphics window, but the 3D model still shows in the spaces where the viewports were.

Fig. 13.33 is an example of a 3D model in 3 viewports in **MSpace** and Fig. 13.34 the 3D model in **PSpace** after moving the viewports and then turning the layer **VPORTS** off.

The value of these operations between **MSpace** and **PSpace** allows the operator to set up a 3D model ready to be printed/plotted as an orthographic projection. If a plot or print is required with the hidden lines of a 3D model removed, use the **Hideplot** prompt of the

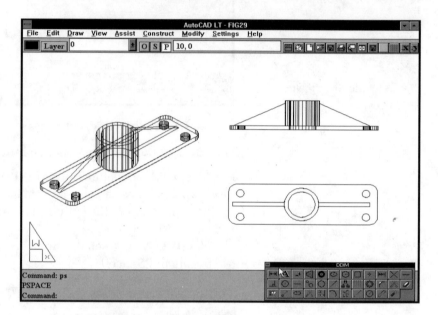

Fig. 13.34 The **MSpace** 3D model taken into **PSpace** with the layer containing the viewport edges turned off.

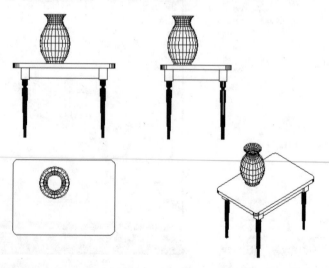

Fig 13.35 A plot of a 3D model in which the viewport edges have been hidden and **Hideplot** put into action

MVIEW command sequence. If with **Hideplot** in operation any edge of a viewport is picked while in **PSpace** the view in that viewport is printed or plotted with hidden lines removed.

Questions

1. In which direction is the +ve Z axis in relation to the AutoCAD LT graphics window?
2. Can a 3D solid model be constructed in AutoCAD LT?
3. What is the purpose of the tool **HIDE**?
4. What is the purpose of the tool **SHADE**?
5. If the response to **VPOINT** is −1,−1,1 from which directions would you expect a 3D model to be viewed?
6. If the response were 1,1,−1 from which direction would you expect a 3D model to be viewed?
7. What is the purpose of the **Viewpoint ISO Views** commands?
8. What is the difference between viewing a model using the **VPOINT** tool and viewing it with the aid of an **UCS**?
9. What is the purpose of **Paper Space**?
10. When a 3D model is loaded into AutoCAD LT will it load into **PSpace** or **MSpace**?

Exercises

Because AutoCAD LT is not equipped to construct full 3D models, no exercises will be set for this chapter. The reader is however advised to load any 3D models he/she may have constructed in AutoCAD and practise using the variety of 3D tools and commands in AutoCAD LT.

CHAPTER 14

The Clipboard and Object Linking

Introduction

Several applications can be opened in Windows to run concurrently. For example, one can have AutoCAD LT, the Windows Paint programme, AutoSketch, Hijaak, PageMaker, and the Windows File Manager as well as the Windows Program Manager all running at the same time, hidden behind all but the program currently in use. In fact, if the windows holding programs are made small enough several can be seen on the screen at the same time.

In addition Windows allows easy switching between any applications which have been loaded from the Program Manager. Switching between loaded applications can be carried out in one of two ways:

1. *Left-click* on the button at the extreme top left of any of the Windows windows. Then *left-click* on **Switch To...** in the dialogue box which appears (Fig. 14.1). The **Task List** dialogue box appears (Fig. 14.2). A *left-click* on the name of the required application brings it on screen.

Fig. 14.1 The Windows menu which appears with a *left-click* on the top left button

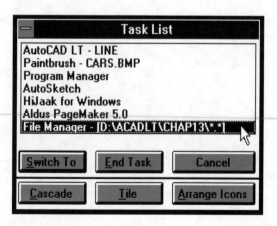

Fig. 14.2 The **Task List** dialogue box

Fig. 14.3 One of the
application name boxes
appearing with **Alt/TAB**

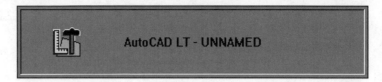

2. Press the key marked **Alt**, together with the **Tab** key (two arrows).
    A name box such as that shown in Fig. 14.3 appears. As the keys are
    repeatedly pressed so the names of the applications which are
    already loaded appear one after the other in similar name boxes.
    Stop pressing the keys when the name of the required application
    appears and its window comes up on screen.

One of the applications included in the Windows software package
is the **Clipboard**. To activate the Clipboard *double-click* on the icon
Clipboard Viewer in the Program Manager (Fig. 14.4). The Clipboard
window appears. The Clipboard is used as a window onto which
details such as graphics and text can be loaded for transfer from one
application to another. With its aid a drawing constructed in AutoCAD
LT can be pasted into a document produced with the aid of a word
processing package such as Write or into a Desktop Program document
such as can be produced with PageMaker. There are several tools in
AutoCAD LT for pasting drawings via the Clipboard into other
applications. These tools can be called from the **Edit** pull-down
menu (Fig. 14.5).

Fig. 14.4 The **Clipboard
Viewer** icon

Types of graphic files

Several types of graphics files can be used in conjunction with
AutoCAD LT. Fig. 14.6 shows the commands needed to load and/or
save those files which are not of the AutoCAD *.dwg type. The files
which can be used with AutoCAD LT are of the following types:

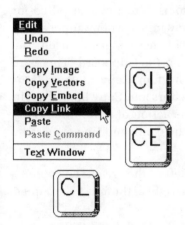

Fig. 14.5 Calling the **Copy**
tools

> AutoCAD drawing files (*.dwg)
> DXF or Data Exchange Files (*.dxf)
> Bitmaps (*.bmp, *.dib)
> WMF or Windows metafiles (*.wmf)
> Slide files (*.sld)
> Postscript files (*.tif and *.eps)

AutoCAD and DXF files are of a type known as *vector* files, in which
the data of the mathematics of the ends, slopes, angles etc. of
individual entities are stored. DXF files allow AutoCAD drawings to
be loaded into other applications which have a load DXF facility.
Bitmap files are based on the data of individual pixels making up a
graphics image. WMF files are partly bitmap and partly vector files.

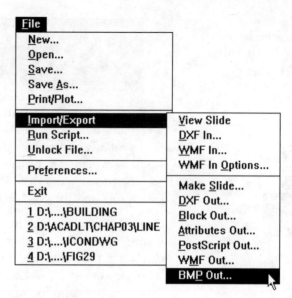

Fig. 14.6 The **Import/Export** sub-menu of the **File** pull-down menu

The COPY tools

As shown in Fig. 14.5 there are four tools which can be called for *pasting* AutoCAD drawings, or parts of drawings into other applications via the Clipboard. No matter which of these four are used, the drawing, or part drawing will appear on the Clipboard. There are however some differences between the four **Copy** tools in their effects, although **Copy Image**, **Copy Vectors** and **Copy Embed** act in a similar fashion. As an example of the action of these three Copy tools, when **Copy Embed** is selected, the command line shows:

Command: COPYEMBED
Select objects: *left-click* to the top left of the area to be copied
Other corner: *left-click* to the bottom right of the area to be copied
    151 found
Select objects: *right-click*
Command:

and the area within the selected window is copied to the Clipboard.

The tool COPY LINK

Copy Link however works in an entirely different manner. All the **Copy** tools are part of the **Object Linking and Embedding** (OLE) facility of Windows. Whereas the first mentioned three of the **Copy** tools can be used to embed a copy of a drawing by **Pasting** in an application, **Copy Link** links the AutoCAD LT drawing to the copy in the application document as well as pasting it into the document.

Fig. 14.7 **Copy Link** of a
drawing from AutoCAD LT
onto the Windows **Clipboard**

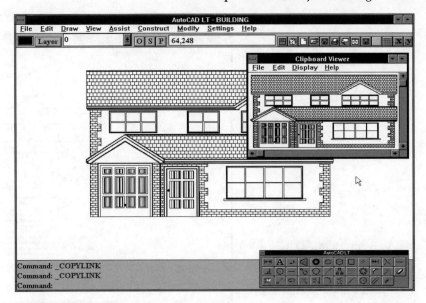

When **Copy Link** is selected from the **Edit** menu (or *enter* cl at the keyboard), the command line shows:

Command: COPYLINK (the drawing highlights and regenerates)
Command:

and the whole drawing is copied to the Clipboard – Fig. 14.7.

The real difference between **Copy Link** and the other three copy tools is that if the copy on the Clipboard is then pasted into a document in an application the drawing is then linked between AutoCAD LT and the application document. Fig. 14.8 is an example of the front view of a house shown in Fig. 14.7 pasted into a document in the desktop program PageMaker 5.

In the PageMaker window a *double-left-click* within the drawing brings back the AutoCAD LT window with its drawing. If the AutoCAD LT program is not currently loaded it will automatically be loaded with the drawing linked to PageMaker. The two drawings are linked together – the AutoCAD drawing is link/embedded in the PageMaker document. Changes made to the drawing in AutoCAD LT will appear in the PageMaker document using the **Links...** facility of PageMaker, providing the AutoCAD drawing with any amendments has first been saved . This form of linking does not occur with the other three copy tools, although they can be used to copy drawings or parts of drawings from AutoCAD LT into other applications. The drawings will not however be linked.

Any of the **Copy** tools can be used to paste AutoCAD drawings in other Windows applications as necessary. It can also be used to **Paste** (**Edit** menu) an AutoCAD drawing into another AutoCAD

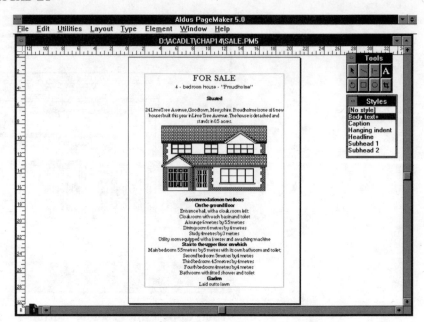

Fig. 14.8 An AutoCAD LT
drawing pasted into a
PageMaker 5 document via the
Clipboard with the aid of the
tool **Copy Link**

drawing. A drawing pasted into another using a Copy tool will be in
the form of a block, which will need to be exploded if individual
parts of the pasted drawing are to be modified.

A 3D model drawing loaded into AutoCAD LT can be copied to
other applications. If the copying is to be carried out so that hidden
lines are removed from the copy, use the **HIDE** tool on the drawing
in AutoCAD LT before it is copied to the Clipboard. Fig. 14.9 is an
example of a 3D model drawing linked to a **Windows Write** document.

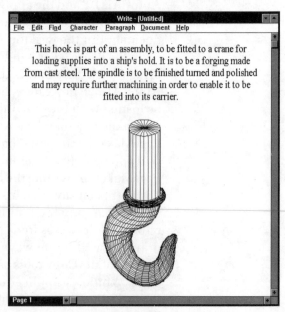

Fig. 14.9 A 3D model with
hidden lines removed
embedded in a **Windows
Write** document

DXF files

Data Exchange Files (DXF) is a type of file format developed by Autodesk, the firm who produces AutoCAD. The format allows drawings constructed in CAD applications which include a DXF capability to save or load drawings for exchange with other applications. As an example, the drawing Fig. 14.10:

1. Was constructed from Clip_Art files in AutoSketch.
2. Saved as a DXF file in AutoSketch.
3. Imported as a DXF file into AutoCAD LT.
4. Saved as an AutoCAD drawing file (extension *.dwg) in AutoCAD LT.

Fig.14.10 A drawing from AutoSketch Clip_Art files saved as a DXF file and imported into AutoCAD LT

When importing DXF files into AutoCAD LT care must be taken not to import into a graphics window which contains parameters such as are contained in the prototype file acltiso.dwg. Thus before importing a DXF file, a new graphics window must first be opened which is not a prototype drawing. This is achieved by a *left-click on* **New...** in the **File** menu. This brings up the **Create New Drawing** dialogue box. In the dialogue box check the **No prototype** box with a *left-click followed by another* left-click on the **OK** button – Fig. 14.11. A DXF file can now be loaded. Failure to observe this precaution may result in the following message appearing at the command line:

Not a new drawing – only ENTITIES will be loaded

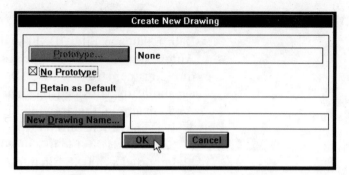

Fig. 14.11 Creating a new drawing which is not a prototype drawing

With the DXF file from AutoSketch each of the Clip_Art drawings is a block. The polyline would also be treated as a block in a DXF file format. As a result if an attempt is made to import the file into a prototype graphics window, none of the drawing would be loaded.

Slide files

Fig. 14.6 showed the sub-menu for **Import/Export**. Two of the items in the sub-menu were concerned with making and viewing slides. An AutoCAD slide file is one which displays the contents of a drawing on screen in a form which can be used for quickly showing a series of drawings at a demonstration or for storing a series of drawings in such a way that the slides can be 'run through' on screen to select one which is suitable for one's current purposes. To make a slide of a drawing on screen *left-click* on **Make Slide** in the **Import/Export** sub-menu or *enter* ml at the keyboard. A dialogue box **Create Slide File** appears in which a filename can be entered. The file will be saved to the given name with an extension *.sld. To view a slide *left-click* on **View Slide** and select the required filename from the **Select Slide File dialogue** box which appears on screen.

Notes

1. Slide files take up considerably less disk space than their relative drawing files. As an example the building drawing shown in Fig. 14.7 required 101,841 bytes of disk space. Its slide file only required 13,126 bytes;

2. Slide files load over any existing drawing on screen. To return to the original drawing either **Redraw** or **Regen** and the slide file disappears.

The AutoCAD LT graphics window

When working with AutoCAD for Windows as many as three AutoCAD windows can be opened together. However when working with AutoCAD LT, if an attempt is made to open more than one AutoCAD LT window a warning box appears on screen:

Cannot Open Another AutoCAD LT

Questions

1. What are the two methods of switching between applications in Windows?
2. What are the differences between **Copy Link** and the other three **Copy** tools?
3. How many copies of AutoCAD LT can be running at the same time?
4. What is the purpose of the Windows Clipboard?
5. What is the difference between a vector file and a bitmap file?
6. If an AutoCAD LT drawing is linked in an application document, how can amendments in the drawing be included in the application document?
7. What is the purpose of a DXF file?
8. What is an AutoCAD LT slide file?
9. What types of files can be used in AutoCAD LT?
10. Can 3D drawing models loaded into AutoCAD LT be copied to another application?

Exercises

These exercises are included here as revision exercises, but the reader is advised to use the **Copy** tools to copy or/and link the answers to any Windows application which is on the hard disk of the computer in use. The following could be attempted:

Copying answers to the Windows Clipboard.
Copying the answers to another drawing opened in AutoCAD LT.
Linking the answers to another application and updating links through the Object Linking feature of Windows and AutoCAD LT.

1. Working to any convenient dimensions and using a hatch pattern and text of your own choice construct a house nameplate similar to Fig. 14.12.

Fig. 14.12 Exercise 1

2. Construct Fig. 14.13 using any hatch patterns of your own choice.

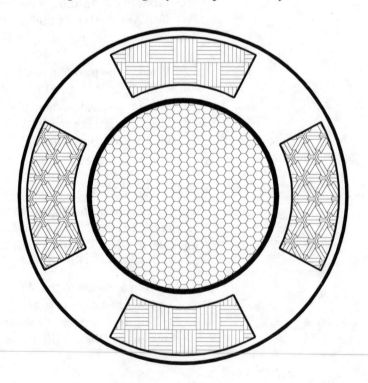

Fig. 14.13 Exercise 2

3. Fig. 14.14 is a partly exploded isometric drawing of an occasional table. Working to a scale of 1:5 construct a three view orthographic projection of the assembled table. Include all necessary dimensions and a suitable title block.

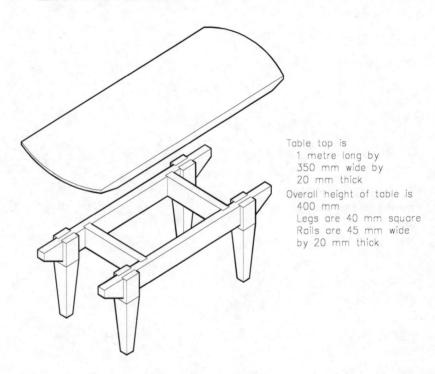

Table top is
  1 metre long by
  350 mm wide by
  20 mm thick
Overall height of table is
  400 mm
  Legs are 40 mm square
  Rails are 45 mm wide
  by 20 mm thick

Fig. 14.14 Exercise 3

4. Fig. 14.15 is a two view orthographic projection of a link arm from a machine. Construct an isometric drawing of the link.

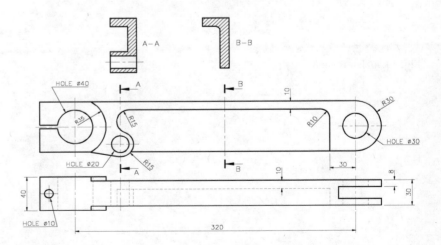

Fig. 14.15 Exercise 4

5. Fig. 14.16 is a 3D model drawing a chain gear wheel and Fig. 14.17 a front view of the gear wheel. Copy Fig. 14.17, add an end view in orthographic projection with the front view and include a suitable title block.

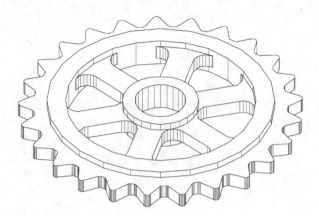

Fig. 14.16 The 3D model drawing for Exercise 5

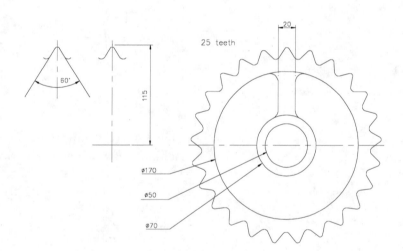

Fig. 14.17 Exercise 5

6. Fig. 14.18 is a 3D model drawing of a casting from a pumping device. Fig. 14.19 is a dimensioned plan view of the casting. The overall height of the casting is 100 mm and its top and bottom flanges are 20 mm thick. Copy the given plan and add front and end view in orthographic projection with the plan you have constructed.

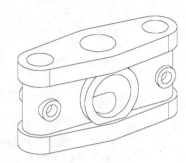

Fig. 14.18 A 3D model drawing of the casting for Exercise 6

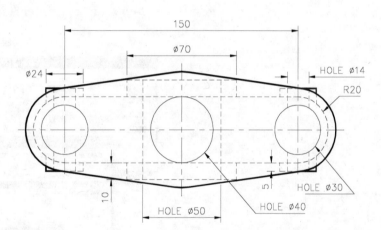

Fig. 14.19 Exercise 6

CHAPTER 15

Printing and plotting

The Windows Print Manager

No matter whether the operator wishes to print or plot a drawing, the same procedure is followed, because either operation is carried out via the **Print Manager** of Windows. The printer or plotter to which the Windows Print Manager is to send the data for printing or plotting is set in the **Printers** dialogue box which appears with a *double-left-click* on the **Printers** icon in the Windows **Control Panel** – Fig. 15.1.

Fig. 15.1 The Windows **Printers** dialogue box called from **Printers** in the Windows **Control Panel**

Once the plotter or printer has been set up in the **Printers** dialogue box, printing or plotting of AutoCAD LT drawings is carried out through the **Print Manager**. Fig. 15.2 shows the **Print Manager** window when an AutoCAD drawing was being printed out to an **HP LaserJet IIIP** printer. Details of the size of the print, the time and the date when the print was made show in the window. As

Fig. 15.2 The **Print Manager**
window showing details of an
AutoCAD LT drawing being
printed

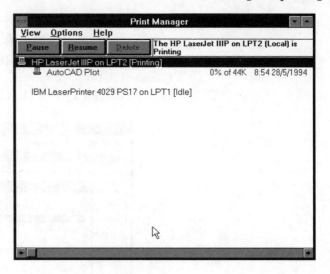

Fig. 15.3 Calling **Print/Plot...**

printing takes place, the percentage of the print data being sent to the
printer is constantly updated in the window.

Printing/Plotting

Left-click on **Print/Plot... in** the **File** pull-down menu – Fig. 15.3. The
Plot Configuration dialogue box appears – Fig. 15.4. The various
settings relating to the drawing to be printed are set in this dialogue
box.

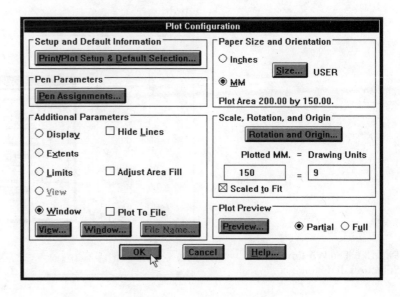

Fig. 15.4 The **Plot
Configuration** dialogue box

Examples of the dialogue boxes called from **Plot Configuration** are:

Fig. 15.5 – *Left-click* on the **Size...** button and the **Paper Size** dialogue box appears. In this box sizes in millimetres or in inches can be entered in the appropriate boxes. In the given example a paper size of 200 mm by 150 mm has been selected.

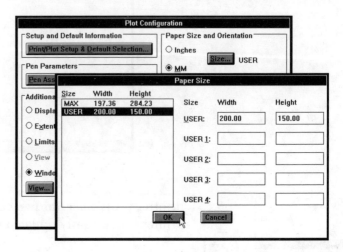

Fig. 15.5 The **Paper Size** dialogue box called with a *left-click* on the **Size...** button

Fig. 15.6 – *Left-click* on the **Window...** button and the **Window Selection** dialogue box appears against the drawing in the graphics window. When the corners of the window in which the drawing will be printed have been selected, the dialogue box reappears against a background of the drawing within its selected print/plot window.

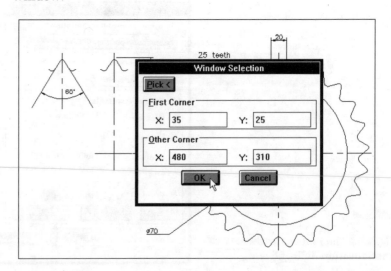

Fig. 15.6 The **Window Selection** dialogue box

Fig. 15.7 – *Left-click* on the circle named **Full**, followed by another *left-click* on the **Preview...** button. The graphics screen will show the area of the drawing on screen which will be plot/printed against a rectangle representing the selected **Paper Size**.

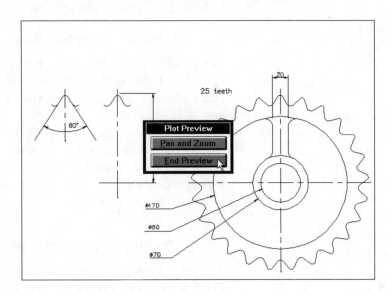

Fig. 15.7 The **Plot Preview** box which appears with a *left-click* on the **Preview Full** buttons

Fig. 15.8 – *Left-click* on the **Print/Plot Setup & Default Selection...** button in the **Plot Configuration** dialogue box, followed by another *left-click* on the **Show System Requirements...** button in the next box. The **Show Device Requirements** box appears.

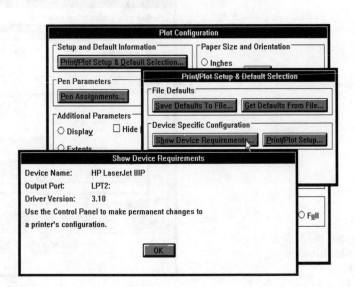

Fig. 15.8 The **Show Device Requirements** box

From these examples, it can be seen that the parameters for printing or plotting are made by settings in the various dialogue boxes. When all these settings have been made, they will not have to be repeated unless the parameters are to be changed. When printing or plotting is started a warning box appears with the message:

Sending to System Printer

The command line shows the percentage of the drawing being sent to the **Print Manager**. When this reaches 100%, the printer or plotter starts producing the hardcopy required. Further warning boxes will appear if something is not functioning properly – for example if the printer is not switched on, if the printer does not have paper loaded, if the wrong printer or plotter has been selected in the **Plot Configuration** dialogue box. If such warnings appear and the necessary steps are taken to rectify them, a *left-click* on the **OK** button of the warning box will start up the printing.

Printing or plotting from a plot file

A drawing can be printed or plotted without using the Windows **Print Manager** by sending the plot data to a plot file and then printing or plotting from the MS-DOS prompt outside Windows. Fig. 15.9 shows the method of sending the drawing data to a plot file. In the **Plot Configuration** dialogue box, ensure that the **Plot to File** box is checked, then *left-click* on the dialogue box **OK** button. In the

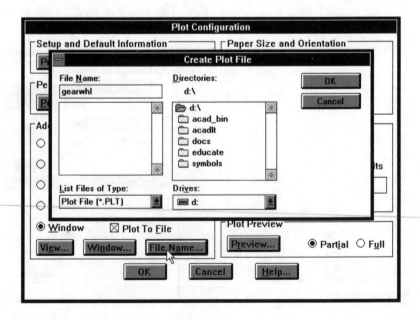

Fig. 15.9 Sending the drawing to a plot file for printing or plotting

Create Plot File dialogue box which appears, *enter* an appropriate file name in the **File Name** box, followed by a *left-click* on the **OK** button of the **Create Plot File** dialogue box. The plot file will be saved with an extension *.plt*. Thus the plot file name shown in Fig. 15.9 will become *gearwhl.plt*. This file can be used from the MS-DOS prompt line as shown in the following example:

C:/> *enter* print d:\gearwhl.plt *Return*
Name of list device [PRN]:_ *Return*
Resident part of printer installed.
D:/GEARWHL.PLT is currently being printed
C:/>

The printer or plotter must be correctly connected to the computer with the appropriate MS-DOS driver for the particular print/plot device properly loaded.

Command abbreviations

Introduction

The following command (tool) abbreviations have been either mentioned or illustrated in the chapters of this book.

A	Arc	DO	Donut	PG	Polygon
AA	Area	DV	Dview	PL	Pline
AR	Array	E	Erase	PP	Plot
B	Block	EL	Ellipse	PR	Purge
BR	Break	EX	Extend	PS	Pspace
C	Circle	F	Fillet	R	Redraw
CC	Copyclip	H	Hatch	RC	Rectang
CE	Copyembed	HI	Hide	RO	Rotate
CF	Chamfer	I	Ddinsert	S	Stretch
CH	Change	L	Line	SC	Scale
CI	Copyimage	M	Move	SO	Solid
CL	Copylink	MI	Mirror	ST	Style
CP	Copy	MS	Mspace	T	Dtext
D	Dim	MV	Mview	TI	Time
D1	Dim1	OF	Offset	TR	Trim
DI	Distance	P	Pan	U	Undo
DL	Dline	PE	Pedit	VP	Vpoint

There are however many more commands (tool) abbreviation available in AutoCAD LT. The remainder of the abbreviations are given on the next page.

Other abbreviations

AB	About	AX	Ddattext	DAD	Ddattdef
AD	Attdef	BA	Base	DAX	Ddattext
AE	Ddatte	BM	Blipmode	DC	Ddchprop
AP	Aperture	CO	Color	DE	Ddatte
AT	Attdisp	DA	Ddrmodes	DM	Ddim

DN	Dxfin	MU	Multiply	SL	Ddselect
DR	Ddrename	O	Osnap	SN	Snap
DS	Dsviewer	OO	Oops	SR	Script
DT	Dtext	OP	Open	TE	Ddedit
DX	Dxfout	OR	Ortho	TH	Thickness
ED	Ddedit	OS	Ddosnap	TL	Toolbox
EM	Ddemodes	PB	Pickbox	TM	Tilemode
ET	Exit	PC	Pasteclip	UC	Dducs
EV	Elev	PS	Psltscale	UI	Uscicon
FL	Fill	PF	Preferences	UL	Unlock
G	Grid	PN	Plinegen	UT	Units
GR	Ddgrips	PT	Point	UP	Dducsp
IN	Insert	PU	Psout	V	View
IS	Isoplane	PV	Plan	VL	Vplayer
LA	Layer	QT	Qtext	VS	Vslide
LC	Ltscale	RE	Redo	W	Wblock
LD	Ddlmodes	RG	Regen	WI	Wmfin
LM	Limits	RN	Rename	WO	Wmfout
LS	List	SA	Save	X	Explode
LT	Linetype	SD	Shadedge	XB	Xbind
ML	Mslide	SE	Select	XR	Xref
MN	Minsert	SH	Shade		

Dialogue box abbreviations

When some of the abbreviations are entered at the command line a dialogue box appears in the AutoCAD LT graphics window. These are listed below.

AX	Select Template File	I	Insert
DA	Drawing Modes	LD	Layer Control
DAD	Attribute Definition	OS	Running Object Snap
DC	Change Properties	PF	Preferences
DM	Dimension Styles and Settings	PU	Create Postscript File
		SL	Entity Selection Settings
DN	Select DXF File	TE	Edit Text
DR	Rename	UC	UCS Control
DS	Aerial View	UP	UCS Orientation
DX	Create DXF File	W	Create Drawing File
ED	Edit Attribute Definition	WI	Import WMF
EM	Entity Creation Modes	WO	Export WMF
GR	Grips		

Function key calls

Pressing the function keys give the following results:

F1   Brings up a **Help** window with help for current command.

F2   Toggles between AutoCAD LT graphics window and an AutoCAD
LT Text window showing all commands and prompts to date.

F5   Toggles Isoplane between **Top/Right/Left** in that order.

F6   Toggles **Coords** on/off.

F7   Toggles **Grid** on/off.

F8   Toggles **Ortho** on/off.

F9   Toggles **Snap** on/off.

F10 Followed by *Return* Brings down the **File** pull-down menu.

Key calls

The following key combinations result in:

Ctrl/C   Cancels last command.

Ctrl/E   Toggles Isoplane **Top/Right/Left** in that order.

Ctrl/I   New drawing.

Ctrl/O   Toggles **Ortho** on/off.

Ctrl/D   Toggles **Coords** between **on/absolute/relative**.

Ctrl/G   Toggles **Grid** on/off.

Ctrl/J   Brings **Line** command into action.

Ctrl/X   Delete.

Ctrl/B   Toggles **Snap** on/off.

Index